ArtScroll® Series

Rabbi Nosson Scherman / Rabbi Gedaliah Zlotowitz
General Editors
Rabbi Meir Zlotowitz ז״ל, *Founder*

Published by

ArtScroll®
Mesorah Publications, ltd

HOWARD KLAUS EDITION

Let's Talk Living Emunah

INSPIRING STORIES AND ENGAGING QUESTIONS FOR THE ENTIRE FAMILY

Rabbi Yaakov Bijou • **C.S. Panski**
adapted from Rabbi David Ashear's best-selling
Living Emunah Series
Project Coordinator **Rabbi David Sutton**

FIRST EDITION
First Impression … August 2020

Published and Distributed by
MESORAH PUBLICATIONS, LTD.
313 Regina Avenue / Rahway, New Jersey 07065

Distributed in Europe by
LEHMANNS
Unit E, Viking Business Park
Rolling Mill Road
Jarow, Tyne & Wear, NE32 3DP
England

Distributed in Australia and New Zealand
by **GOLDS WORLDS OF JUDAICA**
3-13 William Street
Balaclava, Melbourne 3183
Victoria, Australia

Distributed in Israel by
SIFRIATI / A. GITLER — BOOKS
POB 2351
Bnei Brak 51122

Distributed in South Africa by
KOLLEL BOOKSHOP
Northfield Centre, 17 Northfield Avenue
Glenhazel 2192, Johannesburg, South Africa

ARTSCROLL® SERIES
LET'S TALK LIVING EMUNAH
© Copyright 2020, by MESORAH PUBLICATIONS, Ltd.
313 Regina Avenue / Rahway, New Jersey 07065 / (718) 921-9000 / www.artscroll.com

ISBN 10: 1-4226-2722-5 / ISBN 13: 978-1-4226-2722-8

Typography by CompuScribe at ArtScroll Studios, Ltd.

Printed in the United States of America
Bound by Sefercraft, Quality Bookbinders, Ltd., Rahway, N.J. 07065

This volume is dedicated
in loving memory of

Howard Klaus

לעילוי נשמת

חנניה בן אסנת ע״ה

Howie was a man of fine character, principled and honest, with a heart of gold. He was the paragon of "old school" and believed in hard work; you get out what you put in.

He was generous and compassionate, caring about everyone, especially those whom others didn't think about.

Howie loved life, he knew how to enjoy it, and more importantly, he knew how to bring joy to others. He was witty, charming, wise, and had boundless energy. When he entered a room, he brought happiness and laughter. He was magnetic and people wanted to be around him. Gregarious and kindhearted, he truly loved everyone.

Above all, Howie had his priorities in order. His family always came first. He adored his wife Barbara, his children, and especially his grandchildren.

He was loved by all who knew him and will be dearly missed.

Dedicated by
**his wife Barbara,
his children,
and his friends**

HIS WIFE
Barbara Klaus

HIS CHILDREN
Lauren and Lee Kamenitz
Samantha Klaus
and Phil Revien
Hailey and Isaac Barnathan
Allyson and Solomon M. Fallas
Shirley and Jordan Gainger

HIS FRIENDS
Audrey and Eric Adjmi
Corie and Mark Adjmi
Shawna and Eddie Azar
Celia and David Cayre
Joe and Trina Cayre and family
Ronni and Haim Chera
Freda and David Cohen
Norma and Michael J. Cohen
Pennie and Steve Fallas
Celia and Irving Feldman
Marcy and Steven Feldman
Mary and Gary Feldman
Ester and Joey Jerome
Cynthia and Harry Kotowitz
Jack Menashe
Susan and Michael Rabin
Marlene and Charles I. Saka
Lizzy and Murray R. Sarway
Margie and Greg Sarway
Joanne and Isaac Shalom
Sally and Elliot Shalom
Rochelle and Jeff Sitt and Ceilee Sitt

TABLE OF CONTENTS

PUBLISHER'S PREFACE

We are proud to respond to an emerging and growing quest in Jewish life: More and more people are trying to increase their *emunah*. Eloquent testimony to this phenomenon is the enormous popularity of Rabbi David Ashear's *Living Emunah* series. Five volumes have been published so far, and the demand for more is as strong as ever.

This new volume brings the subject into homes and classrooms in a new way. **Rabbi Yaakov Bijou**, an outstanding and imaginative rebbi, joined **Mrs. C. S. Panski**, a distinguished writer and teacher, to present some of Rabbi Ashear's most interesting stories in a stimulating, thought-provoking, novel "*Let's Talk*" format.

A parent or teacher reads the story and asks the children, "What would you do?"

Then the fun — and engaging inspiration — begins. Everyone chimes in.

"I would have done this!"

"That happened to me!"

"I would react this way!"

It's not just *living emunah*. It's *lively emunah*.

As ideas proliferate, the *emunah* sinks in. And when the discussion dies down, the authors of *Let's Talk Living Emunah* offer some ideas of their own. The lively illustrations add more spice.

At the end of the book, the authors present more ideas on how to respond. The result is that we're not just *listening* to stories, but *living* them, and the *emunah* experiences become part of our children and ourselves.

Rabbi David Sutton of the Yad Yosef Torah Center was the driving force behind this project. We thank him for that and for originally introducing Rabbi David Ashear and the *Living Emunah* series to us. He coordinated this project and has given invaluable advice. We look forward to partnering on future endeavors.

The family and friends of **Mr. Howard Klaus** *a"h*, who passed away several weeks ago, dedicated this book in his memory. We are grateful to **Mr. Mark Adjmi**, who organized this tribute to his dear friend. May this publication be an elevation for his soul and bring merit to his family and friends.

This is a time in history when people are anxious and worried, so it's even more important to help our children — and ourselves — recognize that the ultimate antidote to anxiety is *emunah*, the conviction that Hashem is guiding us. This delightful book will help us and countless children recognize His guiding Hand.

Rabbi Gedaliah Zlotowitz   Rabbi Nosson Scherman

Menachem Av 5780 / August 2020

INTRODUCTION

Introduction for Parents and Educators

Welcome to *Let's Talk Living Emunah*, a resource for building *emunah* in children, for both parents and teachers. Parents have an obligation to teach their children Torah, as it says, וְשִׁנַּנְתָּם לְבָנֶיךָ, *and you shall teach your children* (*Devarim* 6:7). However, it is also written, וְהוֹדַעְתָּם לְבָנֶיךָ וְלִבְנֵי בָנֶיךָ יוֹם אֲשֶׁר עָמַדְתָּ לִפְנֵי ה' אֱלֹקֶיךָ בְּחֹרֵב, *and you shall teach your children and grandchildren about the day you stood before Hashem, your G-d, at Mount Sinai* (ibid. 4:9,10). The *Ramban* writes that this mitzvah refers to the special obligation to teach one's children and grandchildren *emunah*. To live with *emunah* is a *mesorah*, and therefore it must be given over from parents and grandparents to their children.

Let's Talk Living Emunah is an educational resource that turns the parent into a teacher of *emunah*. Lessons are centered around five main themes. The reader will encounter carefully selected anecdotes and interesting wonders of the world. Thought-provoking questions, such as "How would *you* react?" and "What does Hashem want us to think?" have been inserted at key points in the lessons. These questions generate dialogue and reflection among the family, connecting the dots between inspiration and real change.

Teaching *emunah* is not only a parent's obligation; it is a teacher's obligation as well. The *Rambam* writes that whenever he encounters an *emunah* topic, he digresses because there is nothing dearer to him than teaching an *emunah* principle.

Whether you read aloud from this book at your family's Shabbos table or teach from it in the classroom, you will find that children naturally soak up *emunah. B'ezras Hashem,* the influence will spread beyond the study session and into the very fabric of family life. With *Let's Talk Living Emunah,* you can help your children cultivate a meaningful relationship with Hashem as you fulfill your obligation to teach them *emunah.*

Rabbi David Sutton

To receive a journal with inspirational quotes especially designed for children to record their personal stories of Hashgachah Pratis, please send a request to:
journal@onlyHashem.com

We would love to hear your personal Hashgacha Pratis stories.
Please send to:
mystory@onlyhashem.com

ACKNOWLEDGMENTS

*L*et's *Talk Living Emunah* combines the vision and talent of several exceptional individuals.

Rabbi David Ashear was very gracious and forthcoming with his material. He read through the manuscript with great insight and attention to detail.

The concept of inserting thought-provoking questions throughout the stories is the brainchild of **Rabbi Yaakov Bijou**. Rabbi Bijou field-tested *Let's Talk Living Emunah* in his classroom at Yeshivat Shaare Torah, and his feedback was incorporated into the text.

Mrs. Chaya Sara Panski crafted the hundred lessons in this book. Utilizing her literary expertise and decade of classroom teaching, Mrs. Panski has made the paramount ideals of *Living Emunah* accessible to the whole family and the classroom.

I would like to thank **the family and friends of Mr. Howard Klaus** for dedicating this volume in Howie's memory. They appreciate the importance of family values and ideals. The book that will promote *emunah* in families is a fitting work to memorialize a man who stood for family and the importance of imparting these values to the next generation. May his memory be blessed. A special thank you to my dear friend, **Mr. Mark Adjmi,** for organizing this effort in Howie's memory. May it bring blessing to his family as well.

I would like to thank the ArtScroll team for its vision and support. **Rabbi Gedaliah Zlotowitz** saw the potential in the original classroom workbook and expanded its reach by turning it into a family and school resource. **Rabbi Sheah Brander** directed the layout of the book with his signature graphic genius. **Mendy Herzberg** coordinated the project, and **Eli Kroen** designed a beautiful cover. I also thank **Yonina Hartstein** for the graphic layout, and **Mrs. Esther Feierstein** and **Mrs. Faygie Weinbaum** for proofreading the manuscript.

A special thank you goes to my father-in-law, **Rabbi Nosson Sherman**, for his encouragement and direction from the very beginning.

Rabbi David Sutton,
Project Coordinator

THE PURPOSE OF THIS BOOK

*T*he purpose of this book is to create interaction and discussion *within the family* on the vital subject of *emunah*. **This book is not meant to be read by children on their own (although they will enjoy doing so and they will benefit from the experience).** For the best results, a parent, grandparent, or older sibling should read *with* the children, or the rebbi or *morah* (teacher) should read *with* their classes.

The book contains many beautiful stories on *emunah*, but we do not want the stories to remain in the book and be deposited safely on a shelf or under a bed. We want them to become part of the child's life. The lessons should be discussed among family members and/or the class. Every story in the book can imbue us all with one of the essentials of Judaism — ***Emunah* in Hashem!**

The goal is very clear. It is to bring Hashem into our daily lives and the lives of our children.

If a child cannot find his or her shoes, it should become automatic that the first thing the child does is ask Hashem for help. When they find the toy they were looking for, they should automatically express a "Thank You, Hashem." When a parent is trying to park and a spot opens up at the perfect time and place, the child and the parent should exclaim, "Wow! What *hashgachah*!" When the grape juice spills all over his brand-new shirt or her brand-new dress, wouldn't it be great if your reaction is, "It's all for the best" instead of, "Look what you did. You're so clumsy!"

We can use this book to train our children, our families, our students, and ourselves to live *with* Hashem — a life filled with happiness, calm, and kindness.

HOW TO USE THIS BOOK

*A*s you read a story, at some point we'll stop you and ask you to pose a question to each listener. You will be amazed to hear the different answers and ideas as you go around the Shabbos table or classroom. These questions are designed to touch on basic ideas in *emunah*. It is important to note that there can be many answers to these questions. A special section of possible answers — from *real kids* — is included in the back of the book. The answers are only meant to be used *after* the interaction has already taken place and the listeners have tried to answer on their own.

By interacting, we can accomplish a higher level of learning, which then becomes a "hands-on" experience. We should become aware of and recognize Hashem's constant involvement in our own lives. Throughout the book you will see a feature called **"It Happened to Me,"** intended to challenge the audience to take their own daily experiences and see Hashem's involvement.

Through this system of interaction, we are preparing our families to deal with any situation that might be similar, in any way, to the story. This is highlighted in a question that will come up often throughout the book: **"Picture yourself in this situation. Think: What would Hashem want me to do?"** At that point, we all imagine ourselves in that situation and challenge ourselves to think about what our best reaction would be — and what it *should* be. This is training in action.

There are five main themes repeated throughout the book, each one touching on a different area of *emunah*.

1. **Wonders of Hashem** — In this section we focus on seeing the great wisdom of Hashem in all the details of creation (the human body, animals, nature, etc.). The goal is to stop to think, and to realize, "It can only be Hashem!"

2. **Hashgachah Pratis** — We want to build an awareness that *everything* is orchestrated by Hashem — to instill in ourselves the knowledge that there is no such thing as coincidence.

3. **Thank You, Hashem!** — One of the ways to build our awareness of Hashem is to recognize and acknowledge the many gifts He gives us. When we say "Thank You, Hashem," we are saying, "I understand that it's all from You!"

4. **All for the Best** — Throughout our lives we are faced with many situations that at first glance seem to be bad. However, we need to build within ourselves the strong belief that everything that Hashem does is ultimately for the good. Through these stories and discussions, our families will *b'ezras Hashem* be transformed and will look at life's challenges in a calm, relaxed, *emunah* way.

5. **Connecting with Hashem** — Here we focus on the ever-important subject of *tefillah*. A key ingredient in *emunah* is to know that Hashem is the absolute, sole Controller of all, capable of anything, available to listen and answer us at all times. Our children need to feel the security of knowing that they have Hashem available to them and that they can always ask for His help, at any time.

The word emunah is derived from the word "uman," craftsman. To become and remain a skilled craftsman, one must constantly train. The great athletes, singers, and musicians never stop practicing and training. Developing emunah is no different. Now, let's start training together!

Rabbi Yaakov Bijou

1
THE VEIL

The town square was teeming with people. A public art competition was about to take place. Two world-renowned artists would present their artwork and a panel of judges would determine a winner.

A special platform was set up so that the crowd could watch the proceedings. The artists and their assistants carried their paintings up to the stage and carefully prepared the display.

At last, the stage was set. Now the judging would begin. All eyes turned to the first contestant.

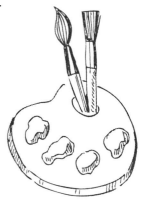

The artist stepped aside and revealed his masterpiece. There was a collective gasp from the crowd. The canvas was alive with vibrant greens and golds. A clear blue sky above rolling hills seemed to go on forever. In the field stood a man with a cluster of luscious grapes. The scene was so realistic that birds flocked toward the stage, pecking at the grapes in the painting.

The crowd cheered and the judges were duly impressed.

The people's attention now shifted to the second artist. His canvas was covered with a large veil. The judges asked him to uncover his painting, but the artist declined.

"My painting does not stand a chance," he said. "My opponent's painting was so impressive, he has probably won the competition."

The judges insisted. "If you really want to see it," the man said, "you can lift the veil."

One of the judges stepped forward to move it aside... but he couldn't, *because there was no veil!* The painting was a depiction of a large veil, so lifelike and convincing it had fooled the judges.

The second artist won the contest.

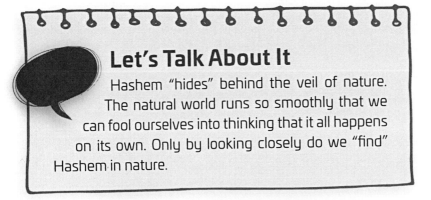

Let's Talk About It

Hashem "hides" behind the veil of nature. The natural world runs so smoothly that we can fool ourselves into thinking that it all happens on its own. Only by looking closely do we "find" Hashem in nature.

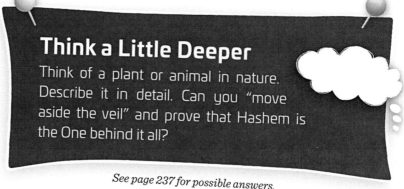

Think a Little Deeper

Think of a plant or animal in nature. Describe it in detail. Can you "move aside the veil" and prove that Hashem is the One behind it all?

See page 237 for possible answers.

2
CASH IN THE TRASH

Shlomo was putting on his coat after Maariv when he was approached by Eliezer, a fellow shul member. He seemed to be a bit uncomfortable.

"My daughter is getting married soon," Eliezer began. "I was wondering if you could lend me some money. I'm short $30,000."

Shlomo felt bad for his friend. "That's a lot of money," he said. "Let me think about it and I'll get back to you."

The whole way home, Shlomo thought about his friend. Eliezer was an honest person and Shlomo felt bad for him. He decided he would pull together the funds and help him out.

When he arrived at his house, Shlomo went straight down to the basement. He had an old suit hanging there and he stored a lot of cash in its pockets. To his dismay, it was not on the rack where he usually kept it.

He asked his wife if she had seen it anywhere.

"Yes, I actually threw it out yesterday," she said, oblivious to the amount of money that was inside. "You haven't worn that suit in years."

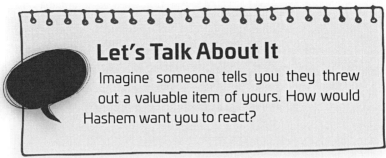

Let's Talk About It

Imagine someone tells you they threw out a valuable item of yours. How would Hashem want you to react?

See page 237 for possible answers.

Shlomo's face turned white. He rushed outside to the garbage bins. Thankfully, the trash had not yet been collected. Together, he and his wife rummaged through the bags, searching for the old, cash-filled suit.

After a few minutes, they found it and breathed a sigh of relief.

Thank You, Hashem, for sending Eliezer to me, on this very night, he whispered. *One more day and all this money would have gone to the dumpsters.*

Think a Little Deeper

When Shlomo found his nearly lost money, he hadn't even done the *chesed* yet. He had only *resolved* to do it. Yet Hashem already rewarded him for his good intentions. Imagine the reward Shlomo will reap for actually helping out a fellow Jew.

It Happened to Me!

Did you ever feel "paid back" for a good deed? Share YOUR *hashgachah pratis* story!

3
SIXTY-FORTY

eb Naftali was married for several years and had not been blessed with children. He decided to go to the Gerrer Rebbe, the Bais Yisrael, and receive the *gadol*'s blessing.

Reb Naftali poured out his heart to the Bais Yisrael. The Rebbe listened closely and said, "Hashem gave you a wife. Have you been thanking Him for that?"

"No," the man admitted.

"Hashem gave you an apartment to live in. Do you ever thank Him for that?"

Reb Naftali shook his head.

"Hashem gave you health, livelihood, a beautiful community; have you ever thanked Hashem for any of these bless-

Thank You, Hashem!: Sixty-Forty | 5

ings?" Again, Reb Naftali replied in the negative.

The Rebbe concluded, "When we pray to Hashem, we should be thanking 60 percent and requesting 40 percent. Go start thanking Hashem more."

Reb Naftali took the Rebbe's words seriously and changed his entire approach to prayer.

A few days later was Rosh Chodesh. As he davened Hallel, Reb Naftali noticed that the words כִּי לְעוֹלָם חַסְדּוֹ, "His kindness is forever," appear six times, and אָנָּא ה׳, "Please Hashem...," is said four times.

It is just like the Rebbe said, he marveled. *Sixty percent thanking and forty percent requesting.*

Reb Naftali continued working on himself and noticed how his life was truly full of blessing. *Baruch Hashem*, he and his wife merited to have children.

Let's Talk About It

Challenge yourself to make a 60-40 list. Think of six things to thank Hashem for and four requests.

Think a Little Deeper

Why do you think people tend to pay less attention to the good that surrounds them than to even little problems?

See page 237 for possible answers.

Great People, Great *Emunah*

Rabbi Moshe Alechsandrov was a talmid of the Chafetz Chaim. Once, during the month of Elul, he overheard the Chafetz Chaim rebuking himself, saying, "Yisrael Meir, did you thank Hashem enough for giving you the *seichel* to write the *sefer Chafetz Chaim?* Did you thank Hashem enough that there are people who are actually learning from it?"

And so the Chafetz Chaim's list continued...

4
SUCCAH OF PEACE

osef Braun wiped the sweat from his brow. He banged in one last nail and smiled with satisfaction. The succah was complete. His family had just moved to a new neighborhood and they were proud to put up a succah in their driveway for the very first time.

Later that night, Yosef's neighbor came home. As soon as he noticed the succah, he confronted Yosef.

"You can't put your succah here!" he yelled. "This is exactly where I park my car every day."

Let's Talk About It
Picture yourself in this situation.
Think: How would Hashem want me to react?

See page 237 for possible answers.

Yosef remained calm. "I'm sorry, I didn't realize," he said. "It's a very big driveway. There is plenty of room.

Can you possibly put your car in a different spot for the next eight days?"

The neighbor was very stubborn. "No," he replied. "This is my spot. Move the succah."

Yosef was upset. He had spent an entire day building the succah with his sons. He thought for a moment and decided, *I will not fight with my new neighbor. Instead, I will give in and rebuild the succah in a different area.*

The very next day, Yosef and his sons took apart all their hard work from the day before. They spent a lot of time and energy rebuilding it a few feet over.

On the first night of Succos, the Braun family ate in their succah, truly a *Succas Shalom*, a Succah of Peace. Moving the succah had been a big job, but they were glad to have avoided a *machlokes*.

After the meal, Yosef and his sons set up beds in the succah. Just as they fell asleep, there was a tremendous crash. They crept out to check what had happened and stared in disbelief. A large portion of the building next door had fallen loose. Their neighbor's car was parked in its usual spot but now it was completely smashed.

The Brauns were very shaken. A few days ago, their succah had stood in precisely the place of the crash. They clearly witnessed with their own eyes how being *mevater* had saved their lives.

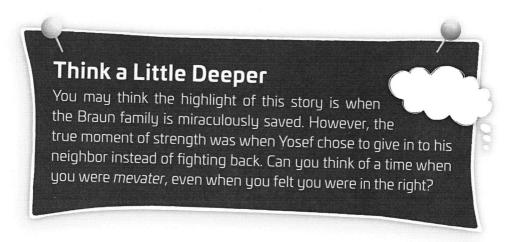

Think a Little Deeper

You may think the highlight of this story is when the Braun family is miraculously saved. However, the true moment of strength was when Yosef chose to give in to his neighbor instead of fighting back. Can you think of a time when you were *mevater*, even when you felt you were in the right?

5
DIRECT LINE

*Y*ehudis and Sima were sisters who liked to play together in the park. They were old enough to walk there themselves and today the weather was beautiful.

There was just one problem. On nice days, the park was always full. Over the last few years, the neighborhood had grown and the playground which had once felt spacious now seemed crowded.

The girls arrived at the park, and sure enough, it was packed.

"All the courts are taken," grumbled Sima. "Look how long the line is for the swings."

"It's a good thing we brought along books to read," Yehudis said brightly.

The girls sat down on the grass to read. They read for a while and then headed back to their house.

Sima was frustrated. "It's not fair!" she said when they arrived home. "We can never enjoy the park. There are so many kids, it's impossible for everyone to have a turn."

Their father overheard the complaining. "Why don't you girls do something about this?" he challenged.

"Abba, we're just kids," Yehudis said. "What can we do?"

"You can try reaching out to the government officials in charge of local parks," their father suggested.

"Can we walk into their office and talk to them about this?" Sima wondered.

"Well, there's a process. You'd probably have to write a letter or speak with a secretary to schedule an appointment. It might take a few weeks or months until they can meet with you."

The girls looked at each other warily.

"Of course, once you have an appointment, you would have to formulate a statement, with arguments and suggestions," their father continued.

"This sounds way too complicated!" Sima burst out. "Even if we ever get to see these important people, we're not guaranteed they will take us seriously."

Abba's eyes twinkled. "Ah, yes. I forgot to mention that after you submit your request, you might have to follow up several times to see if they are taking care of your issue. And, as Sima mentioned, there are no guarantees."

Yehudis and Sima looked defeated. Neither looked like they were about to go through all those steps to try and solve the problem of the crowded park.

"There is a shortcut I can teach you," their father said slowly. The girls perked up.

Abba took a siddur from the shelf and said, "This is a direct line to the real Boss, the highest Power of all. When you daven, you are using a direct line to Hashem."

"You can speak to Him about your issues with the park, school, friends

— anything." Abba said. "You don't have to book an appointment and you don't have to wait in line. Hashem is always available and waiting to hear from you."

Yehudis smiled. "And we can ask Him for the same thing over and over again; Hashem never loses patience with us."

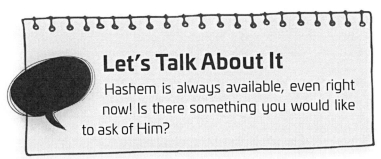

Let's Talk About It
Hashem is always available, even right now! Is there something you would like to ask of Him?

See page 238 for possible answers.

Think a Little Deeper
Even if you don't get the response you wanted, Hashem rewards you every time you pray.

6
THE TONGUE

e can walk, we can breathe, we can eat. But animals can too. What makes us different and greater than all other creations?

Human beings have the unique ability to speak meaningfully. It is one of our most powerful tools. As we are well aware, our tongues make this possible.

What else does the tongue do?

The tongue is the main taste organ. It has between 3,000 and 10,000 taste buds. Salty, sour, bitter, sweet, and savory tastes can be detected all over its surface. Without the sense of taste, eating would be a boring chore.

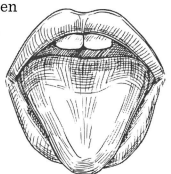

Special muscles in the tongue allow it to change shape and position. This helps us move food around during chewing and swallowing.

After eating, the tongue provides a natural way of cleaning the teeth.

The tongue can flex itself to help produce different sounds when we speak.

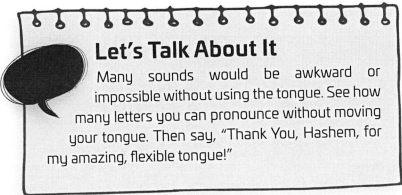

Let's Talk About It

Many sounds would be awkward or impossible without using the tongue. See how many letters you can pronounce without moving your tongue. Then say, "Thank You, Hashem, for my amazing, flexible tongue!"

The tongue helps us fulfill different mitzvos such as learning Torah, praying, and speaking appropriately. Even when we eat, we serve Hashem. In a single meal, you can connect to Hashem by eating healthy, keeping kosher, and making *berachos*. You can elevate mealtime even more by saying, "I am eating this food in order to have energy to serve Hashem."

The tongue is a small, yet mighty organ. It has so many important jobs. Who designed the wondrous tongue? It can only be Hashem!

Think a Little Deeper

Can you think of other mitzvos that involve the tongue?

See page 238 for possible answers.

7
NEVER STRANDED

T he Marcus family was spending their summer in Israel. One day, they woke up early for a full day trip. As they stood on a street corner waiting for the light to change, their little boy Donny tried to run into the street. His older brother grabbed his arm and jerked him back to safety. Donny screamed in pain.

The family got into the car and drove a very long distance. The first stop on their itinerary was the Dead Sea. Donny complained of arm pain the entire time. His parents realized that his arm was probably pulled out of the socket and needed to be taken care of right away.

They were almost at the Dead Sea. "Let's just take one family picture with the water in the background," the father said. "Then we'll go back and take Donny to a doctor."

As they walked toward the sea, they could not believe their eyes. Right there on the sand was their pediatrician from New York! They ran toward him and showed him Donny's arm. In less than a minute, he clicked it back into place.

"You know," he said. "I was swimming here with my children and we were having a great time. Just now, I felt a sudden urge to leave."

The Marcuses were stunned. Mr. Marcus became very emotional. "We are both six thousand miles away from home, and we met here at the exact moment when we needed your help. This was clearly arranged by Hashem."

Let's Talk About It

The Marcus family was prepared to travel for hours to see a doctor. They never dreamed that they would meet their doctor from New York by the Dead Sea. Hashem is much greater than we can imagine, and He arranges things on a larger scale than we will ever understand.

Think a Little Deeper

Why is it that sometimes the story will end like this one, so that we can see the *hashgachah* of Hashem, while many times we don't get to see how it worked out well?

See page 238 for possible answers.

It Happened to Me!

Did you ever find someone or something in a place you would have never imagined? Share YOUR *hashgachah pratis* story!

8
FULL CIRCLE

aakov sat at the table in the small neighborhood shul. He was paying attention to the Rabbi's nightly Torah class when he heard something that made his ears perk up.

"When a person lives with *emunah* and constantly thanks Hashem for everything, even the difficulties, Hashem will show that person revealed good," the Rabbi read.

He quoted a *pasuk* from *Parashas Vayigash*, וְאַתָּה אָמַרְתָּ הֵיטֵב אֵיטִיב עִמָּךְ, and explained:

וְאַתָּה אָמַרְתָּ הֵיטֵב — When you say everything is good, אֵיטִיב עִמָּךְ — I, Hashem, will show you the good.

"I have two older sons who wish to get married," Yaakov mused. "And I am not in the habit of thanking Hashem. I will work on improving my attitude."

Yaakov was very determined. He shared his new mission with his wife. Together they committed to spend time every day thinking about how much blessing Hashem gave them and thanking Him for it all.

Let's Talk About It
Can you share two blessings Hashem put into your life?

See page 238 for possible answers.

Within a few short months, both sons became engaged. Yaakov's home was filled with joy. He decided to share his good news with the Rabbi who gave the class.

He went to visit the Rabbi in his house and said, "I have come to thank you for your inspiring words. They changed my life by shifting my perspective, and through that, I merited a wonderful *yeshuah* for my two children."

The Rabbi was bewildered. "I'm not sure what you are referring to," he said.

Yaakov clarified, "It was the discussion about saying that things are good and thanking Hashem. That class inspired me to change my attitude."

The Rabbi cleared his throat. "Actually," he said, "I was just reading the words out of a *sefer*. I must admit that I didn't really take them to heart myself."

He reached out to shake Yaakov's hand. "I'm glad to hear that it helped you, though."

After Yaakov left, the Rabbi sat down for some introspection.

To be honest, I too can benefit from strengthening my emunah, he thought. He had recently been in the hospital with an ear problem, as he was having trouble hearing. *I too will work on thanking Hashem.*

The Rabbi developed a new appreciation for his life and all that Hashem had given him. After a few days, he received a phone call from the hospital telling him that his chart had been reviewed and there was a procedure that could possibly restore his hearing. The procedure was successful and the Rabbi's gratefulness knew no bounds.

Think a Little Deeper

Why does thanking Hashem help our requests get answered?

See page 238 for possible answers.

9
SURPRISE!

*Y*ehudah was finding it hard to pray in shul with a *minyan*. There came a point when he became inspired and resolved to pray with a *minyan* three times a day.

During that time period, he was also looking for a job. At first, his flexible schedule made his new resolution relatively easy to keep. But after the first month, he ran into his first struggle.

It was the 33rd day of his commitment and Yehudah had job interviews set up for the whole day. All of them were in Manhattan, with the last one scheduled for 4 p.m. Yehudah calculated that it would probably be over after forty-five minutes. This would leave him a full hour to travel back to Brooklyn and catch the last *minyan* for Minchah at 5:45.

The hours passed in a blur of meetings and promptly at 4, Yehudah found himself in the office of his final interview for the day. He watched the clock as the minutes passed. The interviewer was late. Finally, at 4:15, he appeared.

I will excuse myself and leave at 4:45, no matter what, Yehudah said to himself.

The two men spoke about the company and available positions. The interviewer was in no rush and took his time explaining things. Yehudah grew more and more pensive. It was now 4:40 and the man did not seem to be wrapping up.

I need to leave in five minutes, Yehudah thought. *But maybe Hashem wants me to get this job. If I leave, I'll ruin this opportunity.*

He really did not know what to do.

Let's Talk About It
Picture yourself in this situation.
Think: What would Hashem want me to do?

See page 238 for possible answers.

Before he knew it, it was 4:45. At that exact moment the interviewer did the most astonishing thing.

He abruptly stood up and said, "We need to take a break now. The Jewish people who work here use this office for Afternoon Services. We can continue talking in about 15 minutes."

Yehudah was stunned. He would be able to pray Minchah, with a *minyan,* in the very room he was sitting in!

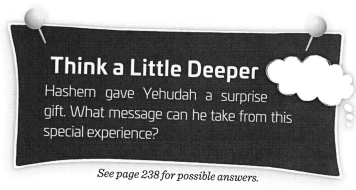

Think a Little Deeper
Hashem gave Yehudah a surprise gift. What message can he take from this special experience?

See page 238 for possible answers.

10

FOREVER INDEBTED

asriel was a wealthy man who loved the mitzvah of *tzedakah*. He could always be counted on to help a fellow Jew.

One cold winter day, he was riding through town when he noticed a pile of rags at the side of the road. He asked his driver to pull over so he could check it out. He was pained to see that it was actually a gravely ill Jew who had collapsed in the freezing cold.

Kasriel instructed his driver to rush the man to the nearest hospital. He hired the best doctors and personally oversaw the man's recovery. Finally, after a few weeks, the man was healthy enough to be discharged. However, he was homeless and had nowhere to go.

Kasriel gave the man a position in his company with a handsome salary. No longer a poor man, the fellow bought himself a home and dressed in respectable clothing. He did so well that he eventually married Kasriel's daughter.

Shortly after the wedding, the new couple joined Kasriel for dinner in his home. After the meal, Kasriel offered his son-in-law a cup of tea. The man politely declined.

"Why not?" the father-in-law asked, curiously. "You always have tea after your meal."

"I prefer not," the groom said, "because I don't want to feel indebted to you."

"What?!" the father-in-law bellowed. "You don't want to feel indebted? Everything you have is because of me. If I had not taken care of you, you would have died a long time ago! Your job, your house, your car, your wife, your very life — it's all because of me. And you're afraid to accept some tea?"

Let's Talk About It

We already owe Hashem far more than we can imagine. What do we show when we pray to Hashem and ask for more?

See page 238 for possible answers.

Think a Little Deeper

Prayer is considered part of the natural system of the world. When we ask Hashem for something and He responds by giving it to us, it is not considered a miracle and our merits are not used.

11

A CLOSER LOOK

Technology companies spend millions of dollars developing more and better products. Every season, there are new upgrades available.

In contrast, Hashem created the human body nearly six thousand years ago, and never has there been a need for an "upgrade" or "Human Being Version 2.0" — we were perfectly created by a perfect Creator.

We can study any part of our bodies and be amazed for hours. A great example is the eye. No camera device will ever be able to do what the human eye can do. Our eyes process millions of images a day, focusing on the important parts of each scene and blurring out the rest. Images are sent to the brain, and the brain decides how to react. This happens at a speed that no device can compete with.

Our eyes also have their own built-in cleansing system. As we look around, tiny dust and germ particles stick to the surface of our eyes.

Do you know how a camera lens is cleaned? The photographer must use a special microfiber cloth and carefully rub off any smudges. Then he uses a handheld pump to softly blow dust particles off the lens. A thorough lens-cleaning can take a photographer several minutes to properly complete. If he accidentally scratches the camera lens along the way, he can ruin it forever.

The cleaning system for our eyes happens instantaneously, and without the slightest effort on our part. We blink about 20 times per minute. Each blink occurs on its own and acts similar to a windshield wiper. The fluid that rinses our eyes during every tiny blink is an anti-bacterial substance that is so powerful, a single drop of it could kill the bacteria in an entire gallon of water. In a single blink, this fluid rinses our eyes, keeping them clean and lubricated.

Nobody could have created such a complex, beautiful, and compact system other than Hashem.

Let's Talk About It
Can you think of another wonderful feature of our eyes?

See page 239 for possible answers.

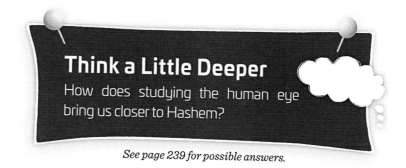

Think a Little Deeper
How does studying the human eye bring us closer to Hashem?

See page 239 for possible answers.

12
BULLET-PROOF
TZITZIS

ico Tousson distributes Torah CDs all over the world. The night before Rosh Hashanah, he approached Rabbi Duvi Ben-soussan with a stack of 300 discs.

"I heard that you are about to travel to Lakewood," Rico said to the Rabbi. "Here are recordings of Torah classes you have given over the last few years. Would you be willing to give them out in different shuls in Lakewood?"

Reb Duvi happily agreed. He drove along the highway at normal speed when suddenly his car veered off course. It dropped over a hundred feet and landed on a road that ran beneath the highway. The car continued moving until it crashed into the metal divider. It folded up, completely destroyed from front to back.

The emergency responders who arrived at the scene of the accident were shocked to see movement inside the vehicle. They couldn't believe anyone could survive such a

horrific crash. The Rabbi was rushed to a hospital. Miraculously, the only injury he had was a sprained finger.

Close family and friends surrounded Reb Duvi when he awoke the next morning. His brother walked in carrying his *tefillin*. "I went down to the junk-yard where your car is," he said. "I climbed in to retrieve the *tefillin*. There were these little sparkling shards all over the place. They looked like diamonds."

The Rabbi thought for a moment and said, "You must be talking about the 300 CDs I was bringing to Lakewood. They're probably all smashed."

His brother replied, "Actually, one CD was left on the chair. It survived without a scratch." He reached into a bag and handed the disc to his brother. It was a class Reb Duvi had given, titled *Where is your bullet-proof vest? Where are your tzitzis?* Reb Duvi then said, "Now, I realize what happened. Hashem caught me and saved my life in the merit of my wearing *tzitzis*. It was the greatest protection, a bulletproof vest to spare my life."

Let's Talk About It

When Rico gave Reb Duvi the 300 CDs, Hashem ensured that the one about *tzitzis* being a protective "bullet-proof vest" would be in the pile. Only Hashem could have arranged that this exact disc would remain whole, while the other 299 were shattered to bits. What lesson can we learn from this?

See page 239 for possible answers.

Think a Little Deeper

This story is full of *hashgachah pratis* moments. Can you find a few?

See page 239 for possible answers.

13
CLOSE TO HOME

$\mathcal{E}$zra Abadi was very excited. From all his brothers, he was chosen to represent the family at his cousin Eli's bar mitzvah in New York. Although he was only eleven years old, he was close to his older cousin and looked forward to spending Shabbos with him. There was just one part of the trip that Ezra was concerned about. He was from a Sephardic background, and Eli came from an Ashkenazic background. Ezra was a little nervous about feeling comfortable in the Ashkenazic shul.

When the big day arrived, Ezra carefully packed his *tallis*. "I hope everything goes smoothly throughout the prayers," he whispered. The trip passed uneventfully, and soon he was in New York.

"Welcome, Ezra!" beamed Eli. The two cousins were glad to see each other. They talked and laughed, sharing stories and jokes.

Soon it was time to go to shul. Ezra reached into his *tallis* bag for his siddur, but to his dismay, it was not there. "Oh no," he groaned. "How will I ever be able to pray the way I am used to?" He went to shul with a worried frown.

When he arrived, he went over to the bookcase to look for a siddur. As he expected, all of the siddurim were Ashkenazic... except one! Ezra eagerly opened the Sephardic siddur.

"Whom can this belong to?" he wondered. To his great surprise, the name in the siddur was *Benyamin Abadi*.

Ezra held the siddur tightly and rushed over to Eli. "Look what my brother Benyamin left in this shul!" he said excitedly. "He was here two years ago for a different bar mitzvah and he must have left his siddur."

"That's incredible," Eli said. "I'm so happy for you! Now you can pray the way you are used to."

Ezra had a thoughtful look on his face. "Look how much Hashem loves me," he said. "He made sure to keep a siddur here for two years, especially for me. He really cares for me to feel comfortable."

Let's Talk About It

When Ezra found his brother's siddur, he didn't see it as coincidence. He understood that everything is planned by Hashem with love.

Think a Little Deeper

Hashem could have arranged any Sephardic siddur for Ezra, yet He prepared one that belonged to Ezra's own brother. This gave the young boy a special feeling of being loved and cared for, even far away from home. Can you think of a time you felt Hashem's special love for you?

14
STALLED

With great excitement and lots of chattering, the Katz family piled into their minivan. They were headed to a family wedding and the trunk was packed with clothing for the next few days.

"Is everybody ready?" Mr. Katz asked cheerfully.

"We are ready!" the children called back. Everyone buckled their seatbelts and the happy group settled down for the long ride. Their destination was about three hours away.

About six miles into the trip, the car started making funny noises. Then it stalled. Nothing Mr. Katz did could get it started again. He tried calling a mechanic but it was late in the day and nobody was open.

"I guess we'll have to take a train," he said to his family. They made their way to the train station with all of their packages. They purchased tickets, and for the second time that day, settled in for the ride. By now everyone was tired and some of the children even fell asleep.

Meanwhile, Mr. Katz looked at the ticket receipt with a worried frown. *This is a lot more than we can afford,* he thought. He decided not to let it get in the way of the family's excitement. They arrived at the wedding late, but grateful to be there.

The Katzes enjoyed the *simchah* and soon they were back home. Mr. Katz wasted no time in having the car looked at.

"I don't see anything wrong with your car," the mechanic said, shrugging his shoulders. "Some switch must have mistakenly been activated. I don't see any other reason why your car suddenly shut down."

Let's Talk About It

The Katz family tried using their van for a long distance trip. It stopped working. They were stuck, so they had to take an expensive train. Now Mr. Katz heard that their car had stalled for no reason and now it's working. Think: How would Hashem want you to react in this situation?

See page 239 for possible answers.

Mr. Katz looked at the mechanic in dismay. "You mean to say I spent all that money on the train for nothing?"

He returned home with his car and went about his routine. Later in the day, his wife was driving slowly down a local street. As she approached a traffic light, she pressed the brake pedal but the car would not stop. Instead, a warning light flashed: *brake failure.* The car continued rolling and bumped right into the car in front of her. *Baruch Hashem,* because she was going so slowly, the car suffered only a small dent and everyone was okay.

Once again, the Katzes' car was in the shop. This time, the mechanic wore a serious expression.

"Brake failure is a serious problem," he said. "Your minivan reached a certain amount of miles and this would have happened no matter where you were. You are lucky you weren't driving any faster."

Now Mr. Katz saw the benefit of his car stalling on the way to the wedding. "Thank You, Hashem, for making the car die last week," he said meaningfully. "If it hadn't stopped, we would have all been in the minivan at highway speed when it reached this amount of miles."

The stress of taking the train and paying for tickets suddenly seemed like a small price to pay for his family's safety.

Think a Little Deeper
We don't always see the benefits of being thrown off schedule. Challenge yourself to react to such changes by saying, "Hashem is the One making this happen. It must be for my ultimate good."

15
ONLY HASHEM!

A group of children were playing together outside. Suddenly, a little boy choked on a quarter. The other children started yelling for help. Someone ran to call the boy's mother. When she arrived, she froze in panic.

The boy's ten-year-old sister approached him and began patting his back, all the while saying, "אֵין עוֹד מִלְבַדּוֹ — there is nothing besides Hashem, there is nothing besides Hashem." She continued to do this until the quarter came up.

Everyone was so relieved.

"How did you stay so calm?" they asked the girl.

She smiled. "My best friend taught me that if I ever feel afraid, I should say the words אֵין עוֹד מִלְבַדּוֹ and everything will turn out fine."

Let's Talk About It

The *sefer Nefesh HaChaim* teaches us that when a person acknowledges in his heart that Hashem is the true G-d and there is no power that exists other than Him, Hashem will remove all harmful forces from the person. How can a person reach such a level in *emunah*?

See page 239 for possible answers.

Think a Little Deeper

Can you think of a time you felt anxious or afraid? In such a situation, focus on the words אֵין עוֹד מִלְבַדּוֹ — "There is no power other than Hashem." This is a wondrous *segulah* that reminds us Who is actually in charge.

Great People, Great *Emunah*

During the times of Rav Chaim of Brisk, the Communists would go from house to house to draft men into their army. When Rav Chaim saw that a group of soldiers had reached his street, he began to say in his mind, "אֵין עוֹד מִלְבַדּוֹ — nobody has any power other than Hashem."

As the Rav repeated these words with great concentration, the soldiers stopped right outside his house for a quick meeting.

"We shall now break for lunch," their leader barked. "Place a marker by this house so that we will know where we are up to." The soldiers sat down to eat and drink. When they were done, they approached the row of houses to find their marker. It was right outside Rav Chaim's door.

"We paused our search by this house," said the soldier in charge. "Let us continue from the next one."

And so, Rav Chaim of Brisk's *emunah* saved him from being drafted into the army.

16
SEASON OF CHANGE

Which season is your favorite? Is it spring, summer, winter, fall?

Hashem blessed us with a world that is constantly changing. Each season brings its own gifts. Even if your favorite season is spring, if you had it all year, you would miss out on the gifts of summer, winter, and fall.

Hashem set up the seasons so that they bring us different sets of wonders. Spring has this way of livening up the whole world, inspiring us to roll up our sleeves and approach life with refreshed spirit. As it gets warmer and summer comes, we spend more time outdoors. Those who are athletic have their chance to shine. As fall rolls around, we tend to spend more time inside. People who are more academic have the opportunity to excel in school. And of course, winter brings shorter days and longer nights when we enjoy the company of family and friends.

Hashem designed the calendar with predictability. This way, we can prepare properly; we know what's coming. We know to get our coats and gloves ready for the cold months. We prepare thinner, lighter clothes for warmer weather. Knowing what's coming helps us be prepared.

At the same time, we never know for sure what the next day will bring. Even with advanced weather technology, there is an element of surprise: Will it be rainy? Sunny? Cloudy?

For everybody, a change of season means a season of change. How wonderful is Your world, Hashem!

Let's Talk About It

Can you think of another benefit of the changing seasons?

See page 239 for possible answers.

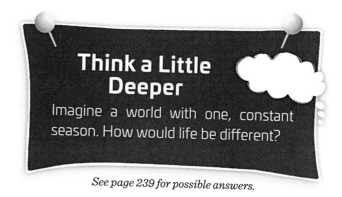

Think a Little Deeper

Imagine a world with one, constant season. How would life be different?

See page 239 for possible answers.

17
LAST RESPECTS

*R*abbi Steven Amon was traveling together with his wife to visit their grandchildren.

"We are only a few miles away from the cemetery where your mother is buried," Rabbi Amon said. "How about we take a slight detour and go visit her *kever*?"

Mrs. Amon liked the suggestion. "That's a great idea," she replied.

They arrived at the cemetery, approached the *kever* and began to pray. As the Amon couple was about to leave, a hearse pulled up a few rows behind them, accompanied by a small group of people. One man from the group asked Rabbi Amon if he would come over and complete their *minyan* so they could say *Kaddish*. Of course, he agreed and even helped them lower the coffin into the grave.

The men thanked Rabbi Amon and turned to go.

"Wait a minute," he called out. "You haven't buried the body yet!"

"Oh, we don't do that," they responded. "The cemetery staff will finish up later." To the Rabbi's dismay, the group walked away from the open grave, leaving the body alone with no one to care for it.

Rabbi Amon was at a loss. Years before, when he was in Yeshivas Ner Yisrael, he had learned that this was a type of *meis mitzvah*. He knew he could not just abandon the unfortunate Jew. Determined, he found a shovel and started digging. For an hour and a half, the Rabbi piled earth into the grave until the burial was complete. He placed the marker that the family had left and took note of the name.

Dusty and exhausted, Rabbi and Mrs. Amon got back into the car and continued traveling toward their grandchildren. The entire time, the Rabbi wondered, "Why did this happen?" He knew the chain of events that had just transpired was not an accident.

He decided to try to find out the identity of the person he had buried. One of the people he reached out to was his mentor and Rabbi from Ner Yisrael, Rabbi Neuberger. He shared the story, including the name that was written on the marker.

"I cannot believe this!" Rabbi Neuberger exclaimed. "I will tell you exactly who this person is. Forty years ago, when you joined our yeshivah, your father was out of a job and could not afford tuition. I looked around for someone to help out. The person who paid for all your years in yeshivah was *the very man you just buried!*"

Let's Talk About It

What lessons can we learn from this powerful story?

See page 240 for possible answers.

Think a Little Deeper

This story shows a *middah k'neged middah* reward. Can you think of a time you experienced *middah k'neged middah*?

18
MATZAH FOR ETERNITY

Reb Shaya was a man of means. He did not have any children, and he wanted to donate his money to a cause that would carry his name and bring him merit.

Should he sponsor a shul? A new wing in a yeshivah?

He wrote his Rebbe a letter, asking for advice.

Let's Talk About It

Donating money is a beautiful mitzvah. There are so many different causes that Reb Shaya could give to. Where would you think is the best place for Reb Shaya to donate his money? Why?

See page 240 for possible answers.

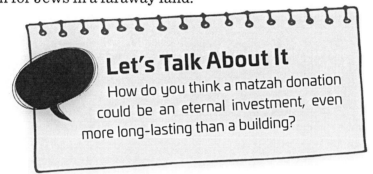

He was surprised by the Rebbe's response. The Rebbe wrote back to Reb Shaya and described the plight of Jewish people living in Russia at that time. He said they were having difficulty getting matzah for Pesach.

"You should use your money to buy matzah for all the Jews in Russia," the Rebbe instructed.

Reb Shaya was baffled. He had envisioned something big, something permanent. Not a one-time food donation for Jews in a faraway land.

Let's Talk About It

How do you think a matzah donation could be an eternal investment, even more long-lasting than a building?

He decided to travel to his Rebbe and discuss the matter with him personally.

He arrived at the Rebbe's home and waited on line. When it was his turn, he brought up his question.

The Rebbe looked at him with a powerful gaze and said, "You want a building with your name on it? I will explain to you your mistake.

"When a building goes up, you can see each brick with your own eyes. It is strong, it is sturdy; it can last hundreds of years. To you, it seems permanent."

The Rebbe continued, "When a Jew does a mitzvah, like eating matzah on Pesach, it seems gone in a moment. Your eyes cannot see the eternal 'buildings' being constructed in *Olam Haba*. That, Reb Shaya, is truly forever."

Reb Shaya's eyes lit up. Sending matzah to Jews in Russia suddenly seemed like a unique opportunity.

"You should know," the Rebbe concluded, "a building that will be used for praying and learning Torah will also bring merit. But children of someone who ate matzah on Pesach cannot be compared to children of someone who didn't. You are not only affecting the people you will feed, but their future generations as well. And all that will be credited to you."

Think a Little Deeper
Being able to do *chesed* is a gift from Hashem. Can you think of a *chesed* you did recently? Say, "Thank You, Hashem, for this wonderful mitzvah!"

ALL FOR THE BEST

19
ONE WORD

Chananya Bergman was distraught. It was Shabbos and his son had suddenly taken ill. The Bergmans lived on a small street in Eretz Yisrael, and just up the block lived a doctor, a secular Jew.

Chananya hurried over to the doctor's house and knocked on the door. "Will you please come treat my son?" he begged.

"I will come," the doctor agreed. "But I don't trust religious Jews. I will only tend to your son if you give me a 500 *shekel* check right now."

Chananya was a learned man and he knew that according to halachah, he was permitted to pay money on Shabbos in order to save a life. He led the doctor to his home and wrote out a check *k'l'achar yad,* in an unusual manner.

The doctor glanced at the check. "Perhaps you didn't hear me," he said. "I asked for 500 *shekels,* but you wrote 1,000." He gestured toward the Bergmans' simple furniture. "It doesn't look like you can afford to pay extra."

Chananya explained. "To write a 500 *shekel* check, I would have to write three words, חֲמֵשׁ מֵאוֹת שֶׁקֶל. For 1,000 *shekels,* I only need to write two words, אֶלֶף שֶׁקֶל. It is worth paying double in order to minimize *chillul Shabbos.*"

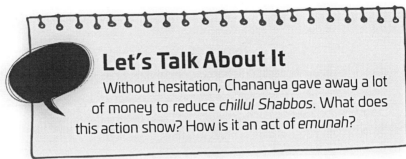

Let's Talk About It

Without hesitation, Chananya gave away a lot of money to reduce *chillul Shabbos.* What does this action show? How is it an act of *emunah*?

See page 240 for possible answers.

The doctor was astounded. He had never seen such devotion in his life. A poor man was willing to pay an extra 500 *shekels* to write one less word on Shabbos! He treated the sick child with utmost care.

After Shabbos, the doctor returned to the Bergman home, humbled.

"I cannot stop thinking about what you did today," he said. "I want to learn more about Shabbos."

Chananya studied with the doctor, teaching him all about Judaism. He started keeping Shabbos and eventually became a *baal teshuvah.*

Think a Little Deeper

Amazing! One person, with one action, made a *kiddush Hashem,* and with that he impacted generations to come.

20
JUST ASK

"Mazel tov, mazel tov!" Family and friends surrounded Shalom Rothman to personally congratulate him. He had completed a *masechta* in Gemara and was now making a *siyum*. It was a momentous occasion that he was proud to celebrate.

Among the guests was Noach, Shalom's brother. He took in the sense of joy around him. He sensed something special in the air and felt inspired to follow in his brother's footsteps.

I never learned an entire masechta, he thought. *But I'm sure I could do it if I had a chavrusa.*

Noach's idea was a good one, but he did not have an actual plan. A few weeks passed and Noach still had not created a learning schedule.

One day, Noach found himself thinking back to his brother's *siyum.*

I really want to make my own siyum, he thought. *But I feel so stuck.*

He looked heavenward and said, "Hashem, I want to learn Torah. I want to finish a *masechta.* If you send me the right *chavrusa,* I will learn with him on a steady basis. I will take it very seriously."

The very next night, he was with a group of friends at a wedding. One of them was a very diligent Torah learner. Noach would have never dreamed of approaching him to ask if they could learn together.

Imagine Noach's surprise when this serious *ben Torah* tapped him on the shoulder and asked, "Would you be interested in learning with me?"

Noach nearly jumped for joy. "I would love to learn with you!" he exclaimed. "I really want to complete a *masechta.* Do you think we could do it?"

For the rest of the evening, Noach walked around with a spring in his step. It was less than twenty-four hours since he had asked Hashem to send him a *chavrusa,* and Hashem had sent him the best arrangement possible.

Let's Talk About It

Hashem loves you. He wants to give you good. Sometimes all you need to do is ask.

Think a Little Deeper

If Hashem wants to give us good, why does He sometimes wait for us to ask?

See page 240 for possible answers.

21
BEAUTIFUL GIFT, BEAUTIFUL WRAPPER

*H*ave you ever tasted an orange? Have you ever eaten a clementine, mandarin, or tangerine?

Hashem created the orange with the most marvelous features. From its brightly colored peel to the seeds within, the orange is packed with miracles. Here are some things to consider next time you hold an orange in your hand:

Before an orange is ripe, it is green on the outside. This tells us that the fruit is not yet ready for consumption. Once it is ready, the green tone changes to a striking, attractive orange shade.

The protective outer peel is a built-in wrapper that protects the fruit from bruises and insects. It doesn't require any special tools; we can easily remove the peel with our fingers.

The slight variations in shape and color tell you what species of orange you're about to eat.

Oranges are pre-cut into individual slices — what a convenience!

The orange comes with seeds for a whole new generation of fruit.

Let's Talk About It

Can you think of another wonderful feature of this special fruit?

See page 240 for possible answers.

Think a Little Deeper

How does studying the wonders in a fruit bring us closer to Hashem?

See page 240 for possible answers.

Great People, Great *Emunah*

Rav Chaim Friedlander once observed how Rav Shach spent a long time looking at illustrations of animals in the back of a *Chumash*. Rav Shach noticed that Rav Chaim was watching.

"Come see how much *emunah* can be learned from these animals," Rav Shach said. He pointed to one of the drawings. "Look at this tiny fly. Notice the intricate design packed into this creature. It is so small, yet it can see, digest, and fly."

Rav Shach looked at Rav Chaim with emotion and concluded, "This creature's body screams out *ein od milvado!*"

22
UNLOCKED OPPORTUNITY

*T*uvia was feeling down. He used to be a successful locksmith, but now business was slow. He had recently moved to a new city and nobody knew of his expert services. Tuvia tried advertising in local publications, but it didn't help.

Months went by, and Tuvia became concerned about how he would support his family. Then one day, his phone rang.

"Is this Tuvia Rosen?" the caller asked. "I found your wallet and I would like to return it."

Tuvia felt in his pocket for his wallet. It was right there.

"It must be a mistake. I'm not missing a wallet," he said.

"This is not a mistake," the caller insisted. "I

have your credit cards, some money, a business card..."

At this point, Tuvia became curious. He headed over to meet the man and see the mysterious contents with his own eyes. It turned out to be an old wallet that his son used as a toy. The credit cards were inactive and Tuvia's little boy liked to play with them. There were a few singles there as well.

Now that the mystery was resolved and the wallet returned, the men started talking. The man was a builder, and he asked Tuvia what he did for a living. Tuvia replied that he was a locksmith, but unfortunately business wasn't too great lately.

"A locksmith!" exclaimed the builder. "You're just the man I'm looking for. I construct buildings and I could use an experienced locksmith. I have enough work to last you a lifetime!"

The locksmith and the builder developed a wonderful business partnership. From that day on, Tuvia had work every single day.

Let's Talk About It

Tuvia tried very hard to find work in his new city. He invested *hishtadlus*, regular efforts, such as advertising. In the end, Hashem sent him *parnassah* in a most unconventional way. This is a reminder that הַרְבֵּה שְׁלוּחִים לַמָּקוֹם — Hashem has unlimited ways of helping.

Think a Little Deeper

This story has several highlights of *hashgachah pratis*: The wallet had cards with Tuvia's first and last name. The man who found the wallet was a builder. The builder needed a new locksmith. Can you find other *hashgachah* highlights?

See page 241 for possible answers.

It Happened to Me!

Did you recently experience *hashgachah pratis* in a surprising way? Share YOUR story!

23
BREATH OF FRESH AIR

*T*oby was a wonderful fourteen-year-old girl. Ever since she was a young child, she had had problems with breathing. Her parents took her to doctors and lung specialists, but none of them could figure out what was causing the problem.

One doctor recommended that Toby go to Arizona, predicting that the dry air would help her. Her parents flew her there, but there was no improvement. Other remedies were suggested but nothing seemed to help.

Toby's family continued to search for a cure for her condition.

At some point, Toby took upon herself to write down ten kindnesses that Hashem had done for her. She committed to doing this every night before going to sleep. This increased her gratitude toward Hashem.

Some of the kindnesses she listed were not necessarily earth-shattering, such as, *Thank You, Hashem, my mother cooked my favorite dinner tonight,* or *Thank You, Hashem; I was a little late to class but I didn't get into trouble.*

Toby continued to write down kindnesses every night, until on the forty-first day of her commitment, she wrote, *Thank You, Hashem, for letting me breathe normally today, just like everyone else.*

Nobody could explain why or how, but her sickness was gone, just like that.

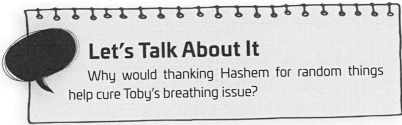

Let's Talk About It

Why would thanking Hashem for random things help cure Toby's breathing issue?

See page 241 for possible answers.

Healthy lungs are a gift from Hashem. They allow us to breathe, speak, laugh, and cry. The amazing thing about our lungs is that we have enough control to take a deep breath whenever we feel like it, yet our lungs continue to function even when we don't pay them conscious attention.

Consider keeping a notebook where you can keep track of kindnesses Hashem does for you. Remember: they don't have to be major! Even the small gifts in our lives come from Hashem.

Think a Little Deeper

Can you share two kindnesses Hashem did/does for you?

See page 241 for possible answers.

Great People, Great *Emunah*

When Rabbi Yisrael Lefkowitz passed away, a member of his family found a folded piece of paper in his wallet. Rabbi Lefkowitz had written a list of approximately forty different diseases — leukemia, diabetes, glaucoma, asthma... At the end of the list, it said: "הודו לַה' כִּי טוֹב כִּי לְעוֹלָם חַסְדּוֹ — *Baruch Hashem* I don't have any of these."

24
BURIED
TREASURE

abbi Eliezer, Rabbi Yehoshua, and Rabbi Akiva used to make an annual trip to the home of Abba Yehudah. Abba Yehudah was a wealthy man and the Rabbis would visit him to collect funds for *tzedakah.*

One year, Abba Yehudah lost all his money. He felt bad about not being able to contribute the way he always did. When he saw the Rabbis approaching his house, he ran inside to hide from shame.

"What happened?" his wife asked.

Abba Yehudah sighed. "The Rabbis are coming, and I have nothing to give. I am so ashamed."

"I have an idea," his wife said. "We have one field left. You can sell half of it, and give the proceeds to *tzedakah.*"

Abba Yehudah followed his wife's advice. He sold the field and brought the money to Rabbi Eliezer, Rabbi Yehoshua, and Rabbi Akiva.

"Please pray for me," he said. "I lost a lot of money."

A short while later, Abba Yehudah went out to plow his remaining half of the field. It was the last piece of property he owned. As he worked with the earth, his cow fell into a pit and broke its legs.

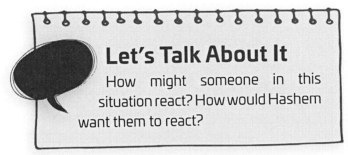

Let's Talk About It

How might someone in this situation react? How would Hashem want them to react?

See page 241 for possible answers.

Abba Yehudah lowered himself into the pit in order to help out his cow. But wait! Something caught his eye. Abba Yehudah leaned closer and uncovered a buried treasure. The contents of his find were very valuable and he became wealthier than ever before.

Think a Little Deeper

Can you think of two lessons we can learn from this story?

See page 241 for possible answers.

25

A SPECIAL CONNECTION

abbi Lish greeted his students with a warm smile.

"Today we are going to do something a little different," he said to his class. "I will tell you a true story about a man named Rabbi Zigelman."

He told his students that Rabbi Zigelman was an upstanding Jew who was serving a prison sentence. He was imprisoned because he refused to betray another Jew. Rabbi Lish described the tremendous self-sacrifice of Rabbi Zigelman. The boys really felt compassion for the Rabbi and the pain he was going through.

"Boys," Rabbi Lish announced, "this is a serious matter. But there is something you can do to help."

The class stared at each other in wonder. How could young boys help a Rabbi in prison?

"There is something each of you can do," Rabbi Lish repeated. "You are not politicians and you are not connected with lawyers or judges. However, you do have a special connection with the most powerful One of all."

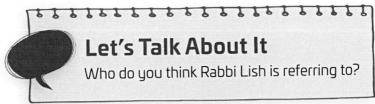

Let's Talk About It

Who do you think Rabbi Lish is referring to?

See page 241 for possible answers.

He paused and looked into the eyes of his students. "Hashem has a special love for the prayers of children," he said.

The boys responded enthusiastically. They prayed intently for Rabbi Zigelman's release. Everyone chose an area that they would improve in as a merit to bring about his release. Then the class wrote him letters of encouragement.

When the Rabbi received the letters, he was overwhelmed with emotion. He wrote back to the children:

To the Young Tzaddikim in Rabbi Lish's Class,

I cannot thank you enough for your beautiful letters. I read and reread every single one. They give me such chizuk. Your prayers mean a lot to me and I am sure Hashem is counting all the merits you are gathering for me.

When I am released, b'ezras Hashem, my first visit will be to your yeshivah *and we will celebrate together.*

Hashem should bless you all,

Rabbi Zigelman

Seven months later, on Chanukah, Rabbi Zigelman was suddenly granted an early release. As promised, he visited Rabbi Lish's class. The students sang and danced with gratitude to Hashem.

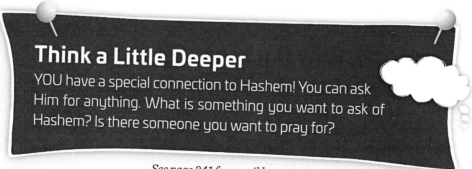

Think a Little Deeper

YOU have a special connection to Hashem! You can ask Him for anything. What is something you want to ask of Hashem? Is there someone you want to pray for?

See page 241 for possible answers.

26
BEAVER, BEAVER OVERACHIEVER

*I*n 1946, the government of Argentina flew in 20 beavers from Canada and settled them onto an island at the tip of South America. The island had a poor economy and the government hoped to boost it by introducing a beaver-fur trade. Beavers eat trees and bark. They build dams made of branches, grass, and mud. The island had plenty of trees and it seemed like a wonderful plan.

However, it was not so simple. In their natural North American environment, beavers chew on aspen, birch, and willow trees. These trees have a natural ability to grow back after being gnawed or flooded. The types of trees that grow on South American islands do not have that ability. A family of beavers could take down dozens of trees in a single night. The island was quickly being destroyed.

Then things got worse. The beavers multiplied and outgrew the island they were originally brought to. They moved out to nearby islands and overtook the landscape. The ambitious beavers left waste and destruction wherever they went.

The Argentines realized they had made a mistake. Beavers did not belong in South America. How could the government get the beaver crisis under control? They joined forces with neighboring Chile. Both countries trained locals to trap and paid them for each beaver. They even encouraged restaurants to serve beaver meat. But these programs only caused more damage. Every time trappers removed a beaver colony from a pond, new ones would move in and build a new dam, taking down even more trees and enlarging the pond in the process.

The twenty original beavers are long gone, but their offspring number close to 100,000. Everyone admits that the beavers are not at fault. Humans should have never introduced them to South America to begin with.

Let's Talk About It

Hashem put every plant and animal exactly where it belongs. If a certain animal is missing in a certain area, Hashem planned it that way. Can you find a specific part of the story that highlights the greatness of Hashem and the limitations of man?

See page 241 for possible answers.

Think a Little Deeper

How can this story reinforce our *emunah*?

See page 241 for possible answers.

27

STUCK ON
THE TRACKS

It was Shabbos morning in Deal, New Jersey, when Eli's Hatzolah radio buzzed. He put his ear closer to hear what the dispatcher was saying. When he realized the call was in his neighborhood, he rushed right over in an ambulance with another volunteer, David.

As they drove toward the scene, they ran into heavy traffic. The trip, which would normally take 45 seconds, stretched for four minutes. When they arrived, they realized that the situation wasn't too serious.

Let's Talk About It

What might the volunteers be thinking at this point? What would Hashem want them to think?

See page 242 for possible answers.

On the way back, David drove the ambulance alongside the train tracks that run through town.

"Why don't you drive on Ocean Avenue?" Eli asked.

"It's okay," David replied. "I'm fine riding by the tracks."

Suddenly, Eli noticed a strange sight. An elderly Jewish man sat in his wheelchair right in middle of the train tracks. His attendant appeared to be struggling to maneuver the wheelchair over to the other side.

"Dave, we need to stop and get out!" Eli shouted. "A train can come at any second."

The two Hatzolah members jumped out of the ambulance and raced over to the scene. They could already hear the horn of an approaching train. With no time to spare, Eli and David grabbed the wheelchair and succeeded in moving the elderly man out of harm's way. Seven seconds later, a train rode over that exact spot. Everyone was shaken by the miracle they had just witnessed.

The attendant explained what happened.

"We had to cross over the tracks," she said. "But one of the wheels got caught. I tried twisting the wheelchair this way and that, but nothing I did could get it unstuck. And then, just as I heard the rumble of the oncoming train, you two arrived."

"Actually, we're on the way back from a call that wasn't serious," the Hatzolah volunteers replied. "Now we see the real reason we came out on Shabbos."

Think a Little Deeper

This story is filled with *hashgachah pratis*. Can you find two examples?

See page 242 for possible answers.

28
CONGRATULATIONS!

ryeh Leib Friedman did not know what to do. He lived with his large family in a tiny apartment. It had a total of three rooms and he felt very cramped. He wished he could move to a more spacious home, but he could not afford to buy anything larger.

Aryeh Leib was so bothered by the overcrowded living conditions that he decided to write a letter to the Rebbe of Lubavitch. He described how his situation gave him no peace, and how his entire world felt dark.

"I live with my wife and ten children in a small, crowded home," he wrote. "We have enough money to live on but not an extra dollar for a larger apartment. This is causing me great distress."

With a sigh, he sent off the letter and waited for a reply.

The Rebbe's response was not exactly what Aryeh

Leib had expected.

"First let me start by congratulating you upon your marriage," the Rebbe had written. "*Baruch Hashem*, it seems like you have a wonderful wife. Furthermore, I see from your words that you own an apartment — how fortunate you are! There are so many people in the world who wish they owned an apartment. I also wish you a hearty *mazel tov* for each of your children. Do you know how many people desperately wish for children? And you are able to pay your bills! *Baruch Hashem*, your life is filled with blessing."

The Rebbe concluded, "Try sincerely thanking Hashem for each one of these blessings. Then see if you still cannot go on like this anymore."

Let's Talk About It

Sometimes comparing our situations to people who have less than us can help us recognize how truly blessed we are.

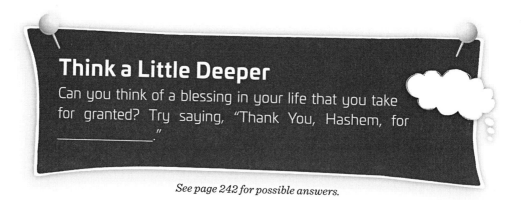

Think a Little Deeper

Can you think of a blessing in your life that you take for granted? Try saying, "Thank You, Hashem, for _____."

See page 242 for possible answers.

29
PATIENCE, MY FRIEND

Manis was determined to start a farm. There was only one problem: he did not know the first thing about planting. He decided to observe an experienced farmer up close.

On the very first day, Manis accompanied the farmer to a beautiful patch of grass. He watched him climb into a tractor and plow the earth.

Manis was confused. "Why are you destroying the grass?" he called out. "Your tractor is turning everything to dirt."

"Just be patient," the farmer replied. "Wait and see."

Then the farmer tossed wheat kernels into the earth.

"What are you doing?" Manis wondered aloud. "You are dirtying the seeds."

"Have patience, my friend," the farmer said.

Over the next few weeks, wheat stalks grew all over the field. Manis watched them grow taller and stronger. *Now I understand,* he thought to himself. But not for long.

Soon the farmer headed into the field with a large, curved knife.

"This is a sickle," he explained. "I will use it to cut down the wheat."

"Cut down the wheat?!" Manis exclaimed. "The field is finally looking good again. Why ruin it?"

But the farmer only said, "Wait a bit more and you will soon see."

He gathered the wheat and placed the kernels between two large stones. Manis looked on with horror as the farmer ground the kernels into a fine white powder.

"You are grinding all your hard work to dust," he moaned.

By now he knew what the farmer would say. "I am trying to be patient," Manis protested, "but every time you have something beautiful, you go ahead and destroy it."

The farmer smiled. "In just a little while you will understand everything."

He poured water into the white powder and kneaded it into dough. He pounded and stretched and formed a loaf. Then he placed it into the oven.

Manis was at a loss. "I was beginning to appreciate this strange process," he said. "But I cannot fathom why you would burn all your hard work."

"Patience, my friend," the farmer said. "We are almost there."

A short while later, the farmer took the fresh, crispy bread out of the oven. Manis' mouth started to water.

And then he understood everything.

Let's Talk About It

How is this story a *mashal* for כָּל מַה דְּעָבִיד רַחֲמָנָא לְטָב עָבִיד — "Everything Hashem does is for the best"?

See page 242 for possible answers.

30
THE IMPOSSIBLE

*R*abbi Yitzchak Zilberstein faced the room of Jewish doctors. He was about to deliver a class on medical halachah, when one of the doctors approached him and said, "I want to show the Rav this siddur." He then related the following story.

The auditorium was filled with proud parents and grandparents. Five-year-olds lined the stage, faces aglow and costumes shining in the bright lights. Today was the day of their much anticipated siddur celebration.

The boys sang with all their hearts. They sang about their joy at being able to read *alef beis* and the great *simchah* of receiving their first siddur. One especially moving song was about the unique power of the prayers of a child.

Among the families in the audience, there was one couple who seemed to be more emotional than the rest. They were the parents of Shaul, whom they had adopted as a newborn baby. This boy meant everything to them; he was their entire world.

The performance came to a close and the audience clapped. Each little boy ran over to join his family.

"*Mazel tov*, Shaul!" said his father, shaking his hand and smiling broadly.

"You did a wonderful job on stage, *tzaddik'l*," his mother added. "The songs were beautiful."

Shaul grasped his siddur tightly and turned to his parents, an earnest look on his face.

"Abba, Ima; now I can pray for something I want so badly. I am going to pray to Hashem for a baby brother." His eyes shone bright and pure.

Shaul's parents swallowed hard and exchanged a look. They had been told by many expert doctors that it was impossible for them to have a child.

"Yes, my dear son. Go pray," Shaul's father said. His voice was heavy with emotion. "Pray, Shaul. Hashem loves the prayers of little children."

That same year, Shaul's prayers were answered and his parents gave birth to a healthy baby boy.

That siddur became very precious to the family. It was a reminder to them that *tefillah* can accomplish the "impossible"... especially the prayers of a child.

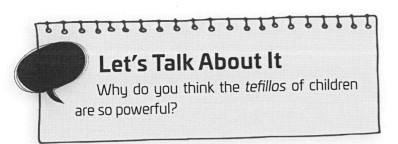

Let's Talk About It

Why do you think the *tefillos* of children are so powerful?

See page 242 for possible answers.

Think a Little Deeper

Think of someone or something you care about deeply. You can pray from a siddur, *Tehillim*, or straight from your heart! Your prayer can shake the heavens and produce real results.

It is important to remember that even if you don't see the results you wanted, no prayer ever goes to waste. It only means that Hashem is saving it for another time.

31
SLOWLY
BUT SURELY

It was a stormy winter night, but inside the Levy home, all was cozy and warm. The children were gathered around a board game in the living room. It was Sarala's turn when suddenly the lights flickered and went out.

"Hey!" she cried. "What's going on?"

Mrs. Levy entered the room. "It seems like we have a blackout. An electric wire must have come down in the storm." She turned on some flashlights and Sarala felt her eyes adjust to the dark. The kids could see each other now but there were dark shadows everywhere.

"I'm scared," Zevi whimpered. He was only three years old. Mrs. Levy held him close.

"It's almost time for bed anyway," she said. "Let's get you into pajamas."

The older Levy kids resumed their game by the light of a flashlight.

Sarala turned to Mindy. "Imagine every night the sun would set abruptly, like a blackout," she mused.

Mindy shuddered. "That would be scary," she said. "People would be walking and driving outside, and all of a sudden everything would go dark. It would be scary and dangerous. Fortunately, the sun takes its time going down and we have a chance to get ready for the night."

"Not only that, sunset is also pretty," Sarala added. "The sky and clouds turn beautiful colors, changing every minute."

The game ended and the girls packed the pieces back into the box.

Just then the electric turned back on. Both sisters blinked in the sudden light.

"It's a good thing the sun rises gradually too," they laughed.

Let's Talk About It

The schedule of the sun is something we usually take for granted. Consider these points:

Hashem causes the sun to rise and set gradually, giving us time to transition from night to day and day to night.

The brightness of the morning sun fills us with energy to start our day.

When the sun sets, our bodies are signaled to start winding down and our energy levels decrease. This helps us slow down and fall asleep.

Think a Little Deeper

Can you think of another process in nature that happens gradually, and how this is a gift?

See page 242 for possible answers.

32
NEVER FORGOTTEN

When the Chazon Ish was a young man living in Kosava, Lithuania, he once needed to borrow money. He approached a friend who happily helped him out. A short while later, the Chazon Ish was ready to pay the debt, but he could not locate the lender.

The Chazon Ish asked everyone he knew if they had seen the boy. He even inquired from people who lived in surrounding towns and villages, but nobody recognized the lender's name. It seemed as though he had vanished.

Let's Talk About It

Picture yourself in a similar situation. How would Hashem want you to react?

See page 242 for possible answers.

The Chazon Ish never forgot this childhood loan. Even when he moved to Bnei Brak in Eretz Yisrael, it continued to weigh heavily on his mind.

When the Chazon Ish passed away, notices went up on bulletin boards all across the country. A Jew in Tel Aviv recognized the name Avraham Yeshayah Karelitz from his youth. This man was not religious and he did not know that his childhood friend had become a great Torah sage. He decided to travel to Bnei Brak to visit the Karelitz family during *shivah* for old times' sake.

The man walked in and sat across from the Chazon Ish's brother, Rav Meir. The man was dressed noticeably different than the rest of the crowd, and Rav Meir asked him who he was. He introduced himself and said, "I knew your brother back in Kosava."

Rav Meir jumped up from his chair and cried out, "His whole life, my brother worried about the money he owed you. He searched and searched for you, and now you are here!"

Rav Meir was overcome with emotion and immediately settled the debt.

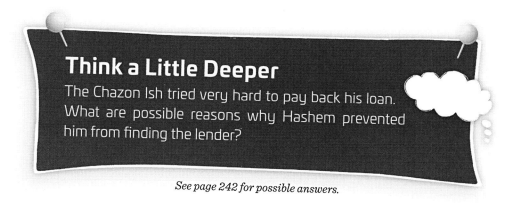

Think a Little Deeper
The Chazon Ish tried very hard to pay back his loan. What are possible reasons why Hashem prevented him from finding the lender?

See page 242 for possible answers.

33
NO NEWS
IS GOOD NEWS

"**S**habbat Shalom, Shabbat Shalom!"

It was Shabbos morning, and davening had just ended in a small Israeli shul. Men and boys greeted each other joyfully as they headed to a side room of the shul for the weekly *kiddush*. This week's *kiddush* was sponsored by Meir Weiss.

"I want to publicly thank Hashem for the *refuah sheleimah* he gave me," announced Meir. "I recently recovered from a serious illness and I am donating the *kiddush* this morning to show my gratefulness to Hashem."

This news was greeted with wishes of *l'chaim* and *baruch rofei cholim*. Meir's friends joined him in celebrating his happy news.

The next week, the shul's congregants once again gathered after davening. The *kiddush* donor of the week was Yaakov Kagan. Yaakov stood up to speak and the crowd hushed.

"Some of you may have heard that I was in a terrible car accident this week," Yaakov said. "My car was completely smashed and nothing of it remained. I was inspired to sponsor this week's *kiddush* because miraculously, I came out without a scratch."

Yaakov's fellow shul members crowded around to shake his hand, and the words *"Baruch Hashem"* were on everyone's lips.

The following week's *kiddush* was donated by a family who had had a fire in their house. Everyone got out safely and they wanted to publicly express their thanks to Hashem. A week later, Nachum Cohen had a complicated surgery that was successful and decided to dedicate a *kiddush* for that.

This pattern continued, with members of the shul taking the opportunity to sponsor *kiddush* and share their personal "Thank You, Hashem" stories.

One week, the *kiddush* donor was Eliezer Neuman. He got up to speak and everyone quieted down to hear what he had gone through.

"I've been listening to all of the speeches this year and I am very inspired," he said. "I don't have any miracle to tell you about. I was not saved from any difficult circumstance. I am sponsoring today's *kiddush* to thank Hashem that I don't have any sicknesses, I was not in any car crashes, and my house never caught fire. *Baruch Hashem,* everything is running smoothly."

Let's Talk About It
Why do you think we tend to take problem-free days for granted?

See page 243 for possible answers.

Think a Little Deeper
Can you think of three blessings you currently have? Take a moment to say, "*Baruch Hashem* for things that seem normal!"

See page 243 for possible answers.

Thank You, Hashem!: No News Is Good News | 73

34
HONESTY PAYS

ivkah Drew was very excited to be sitting in the driver's seat. She had recently gotten her driver's permit, and her mother agreed to accompany her on a short trip to the grocery. As she drove, Rivkah switched lanes without noticing a car coming up in the lane right beside her. There was a small collision that caused damage to both cars.

Both drivers pulled over to the side of the road. Rivkah realized that she had not yet been added to the family insurance plan. This meant that the damage to both cars would not be covered by insurance, and all repair costs would have to be paid for by the Drews.

The other driver felt terrible. He made a suggestion to Mrs. Drew. He said, "Why don't you put into the report that you were the one driving the car at the time of the accident, instead of your daughter? This way your insurance policy will kick in and you won't have to pay a penny!" He seemed pleased with his little plan.

Later that day, Rivkah returned home and shared the whole story with her father. When she told him about the other driver's great plan, his response was adamant.

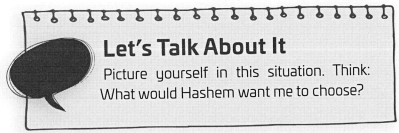

Let's Talk About It

Picture yourself in this situation. Think: What would Hashem want me to choose?

See page 243 for possible answers.

"Absolutely not," he said. "That would be dishonest. Money comes and goes, and it's all from Hashem. We don't need to get involved in anything shady. We will go about this honestly and truthfully, whatever it costs."

Two days later, the Drew family's car was parked on the street. A vehicle passed through and swerved, pushing their car straight into a tree. The very same side of the car that had been ruined two days before was now completely destroyed.

The vehicle owner was very apologetic. He assured the Drews that he would take responsibility for complete repair of the car.

Think a Little Deeper

How does acting honestly show *emunah* in Hashem?

See page 243 for possible answers.

Let's Reframe With *Emunah* Glasses

Imagine your teacher returns a test with a big 90 percent written on top. As you look through the questions, you find one where you wrote the wrong answer but still received credit. If you don't say anything, the teacher will never know. It seems that acting with honesty will cause you to lose out.

What would Hashem want you to do?

35
BRING BACK JACK

It was the night of Simcha's bar mitzvah. Family and friends joyfully filled the hall, shaking hands with the beaming bar mitzvah boy. Simcha had a cousin, Jack, who had grown up in a religious family. Unfortunately, he no longer kept Torah and mitzvos. He showed up at Simcha's bar mitzvah with a loud suit and tie. A tiny kippah was perched atop his wild mop of hair. He didn't seem to care that he stood out in the crowd.

The music began and the guests gathered round to dance. Jack had always loved dancing, so he went right into the middle and danced with the bar mitzvah boy.

Soon Simcha's rebbi walked into the hall. He showered the bar mitzvah boy with blessings for success in his Torah learning and *yiras Shamayim,* and danced enthusiastically. He also danced with Simcha's father, telling him what a wonderful son he had.

Then the rebbi noticed Jack. It was hard

not to notice Jack. The rebbi walked right over to him, grabbed his hands, and started dancing passionately with him. Jack was a good dancer, and the two of them kept going and going.

Exhausted, the rebbi finally threw up his hands. He clapped his new friend on the shoulder and said, "Wow, that was great. I'm Simcha's rebbi. Who are you?"

"I'm Jack, Simcha's cousin. Our families are really close."

"Nice to meet you, Jack," the rebbi said. Then he left the hall.

The next morning, the tired rebbi walked into class and said, "Boys, last night we attended Simcha's bar mitzvah. I had the opportunity to dance with his cousin who is unfortunately no longer religious. He's a nice, sweet boy, but he is really very lost. Boys, I need you to help me bring him back."

The boys looked up at their rebbi, confused.

"We're just a bunch of seventh graders," a student said. "How are we supposed to bring back Jack?"

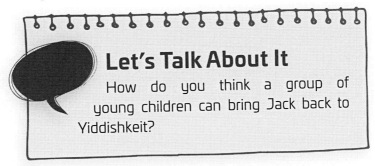

Let's Talk About It
How do you think a group of young children can bring Jack back to Yiddishkeit?

See page 243 for possible answers.

But their rebbi knew exactly what needed to be done.

"We are all going to stand up now and say *Tehillim* for Simcha's cousin. No *tefillah* ever goes unanswered. Let us daven to Hashem to help this lost soul return to Him."

The boys did as their rebbi instructed. They stormed the heavens, begging Hashem to bring back Simcha's cousin to a life of Torah.

Just a few days later, Jack felt an urge to go to Israel and learn Torah. He went to the barber, cut off his long hair, and took the next flight to Eretz Yisrael.

When the rebbi heard this news, he made a party for his class, congratulating them on their role in Jack's *teshuvah*.

Jack spent a full year learning Torah. He settled down and married a religious woman. He is now raising a family of children who bring him much *nachas*.

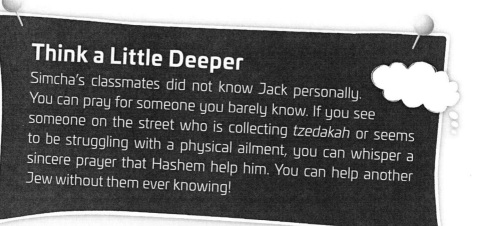

Think a Little Deeper

Simcha's classmates did not know Jack personally. You can pray for someone you barely know. If you see someone on the street who is collecting *tzedakah* or seems to be struggling with a physical ailment, you can whisper a sincere prayer that Hashem help him. You can help another Jew without them ever knowing!

36
WHO IS IN CHARGE?

*A*s a young child, Avraham Avinu lived among people who believed the world was controlled by the sun, moon, and stars. Everyone around him served idols, believing they held power. But young Avraham used his own thinking skills and asked some basic questions.

If the sun is the ruler of the world, why does it go away at night?

If the moon is the true ruler, how does the sun outshine it throughout the day?

Who is in charge of the rotation of these lights?

And so, at the age of 3, Avraham came to the obvious conclusion that there had to be a Creator Who created the sun, moon, and everything else in the world.

Looking around the world today, we can ask questions similar to our forefather Avraham. Who created the trees? Who makes the grass grow?

Let's Talk About It

What other questions can we ask about the world?

See page 243 for possible answers.

Of course, we will find the same answer as young Avraham did so many years ago:

There must be a Creator Who made all this. And it must be that He continues to be involved with His creations every moment.

Think a Little Deeper

Once we recognize Hashem as the Creator of the world, we ask ourselves, "Why did Hashem create all this? Why did He create me? What is the purpose of it all?" Can you try to answer these questions?

See page 243 for possible answers.

Great People, Great *Emunah*

Someone once asked Rav Avigdor Miller, "How do I avoid getting angry when things do not work out the way I planned?" Rabbi Miller responded that when things don't go according to plan, Hashem is teaching us that He is the One Who is truly in charge. At such a time, when Hashem is reminding us that He is in control, it is actually very comforting. How can we get angry?

37
LUNCH DILEMMA

amar had just concluded a business meeting in Manhattan. She decided to pick up lunch before driving home. She passed a pizza shop and thought about stopping in.

Nah, she said to herself. *I'm not in the mood for pizza.*

She continued along, looking out for kosher food establishments. Then she noticed a sushi restaurant.

Should I get sushi? she asked herself. *No, I don't want sushi right now. But I don't want a fleishig lunch either. What will I eat?*

Let's Talk About It

Not knowing what to get for lunch is a small problem. Yet we know that everything has a purpose. What can be the point of Tamar's indecisiveness?

See page 243 for possible answers.

Finding lunch was becoming a bigger deal than Tamar had expected. Suddenly, she felt a craving for chicken salad. Even though a minute ago she did *not* want *fleishigs,* she now headed over to Kosher Delight. She walked in, and sitting right there was her best friend, Dina.

"Dina!" she exclaimed. "It's so nice to see you. What brings you here?"

Tamar noticed that her friend was reciting *Tehillim.* As soon as she finished, Dina smiled and said, "I rarely come to Manhattan, and I don't like taking the subway. I was just praying, asking Hashem to send me a ride back to Brooklyn."

"Wow," Tamar said. "I was having the hardest time figuring out what to buy for lunch. Hashem led me right here. I would be thrilled to drive you home!"

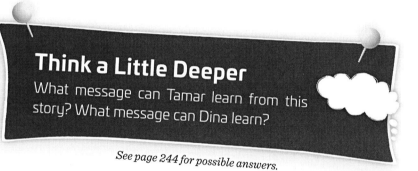

Think a Little Deeper

What message can Tamar learn from this story? What message can Dina learn?

See page 244 for possible answers.

It Happened to Me!

Did you ever experience a small inconvenience? Did you merit to see how it was really for a purpose? Share YOUR *hashgachah pratis* story!

38
SAVED BY THE QUEEN

Baruch was a wealthy Jew who owned an inn in a small Polish city. At that time, Poland was under Russian rule.

One evening, a group of Russian soldiers passed through the area where Baruch lived. The general was in a sour mood and ordered his soldiers to bring him some wine. They made their way over to the Jewish innkeeper.

"Would you sell us some strong wine to lift our general's spirits?" they asked.

"I cannot sell you anything tonight," Baruch said. "Tonight is my Sabbath and I do not conduct business on the Sabbath. But please tell the general that he is welcome to come and take anything he wishes."

When the general heard Baruch's message, he became very angry. He strode up to the innkeeper's door and banged loudly.

"How dare you refuse to sell wine to the general of the Russian army!" he bellowed. "Do you realize the gravity of the crime you are choosing to commit?"

Baruch remained calm. "These are the laws of G-d. I am not permitted to sell anything tonight. However, I invite you to join my Shabbos meal and drink to your heart's desire."

Let's Talk About It

How does *emunah* help us do mitzvos and stay far away from *aveiros*?

See page 244 for possible answers.

The general softened and entered Baruch's home. He sat down and enjoyed the fine food and wine. By the time the meal was over, he was satisfied. He was also impressed with the innkeeper's commitment to his religion.

Several years later, Baruch the innkeeper was falsely accused of spying against his country. He was arrested and thrown into prison. One day, a government official visited the jail and requested to see the inmates. He walked into Baruch's cell and let out a small cry.

"You are the innkeeper who provided me with unlimited wine at no cost," he exclaimed. Baruch rubbed his eyes in disbelief. It was the general who had joined his Shabbos meal all those years ago!

"I was promoted to a higher position," the official said. "I now declare you a free man."

Baruch returned home to his family. His wife was overjoyed to see him alive and well.

"How did you get out of jail?" she asked.

"The queen intervened on my behalf," he said.

"Which queen?" asked his wife.

"The Shabbos Queen," Baruch replied with a smile.

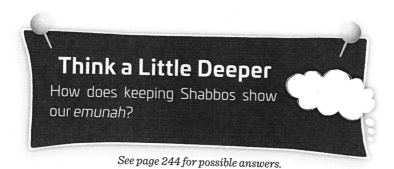

Think a Little Deeper

How does keeping Shabbos show our *emunah*?

See page 244 for possible answers.

39
ABSOLUTE FAITH

Zalman was a fellow who really tried his best. Yet whatever he did to earn a living, he only had enough for the barest necessities.

One day, Zalman was summoned to appear before his Rebbe. A faithful and devoted student, he rushed over immediately.

"Zalman," the Rebbe said, "I am asking you to bring me two hundred rubles."

The poor man was stunned. He had nothing close to that sum. But out of respect for the Rebbe, he went out and raised the full amount.

A few days after delivering the money, Zalman was again asked to come see the Rebbe. The Rebbe asked him to bring another two hundred rubles.

Let's Talk About It
What might be going through Zalman's mind? What can he tell himself in order to strengthen his *emunah*?

See page 244 for possible answers.

The dedicated student did not ask any questions. Although it was very difficult, he once again went around collecting money. This time it took a bit longer, but in the end, he was successful.

When the Rebbe repeated his request a third time, Zalman was not sure he would be able to raise so much money again. He traveled to another town and spent days and nights going from door to door. Finally, he raised enough and presented the funds to the Rebbe.

Soon Zalman continued with his day-to-day life. He now faced a different challenge. He had a daughter of marriageable age, but no money to marry her off. He decided to seek the advice of his Rebbe.

The Rebbe listened to the poor man's problem and said, "My dear Zalman, I knew you were going to have this problem. That is why I had you collect six hundred rubles. Here, I saved them for you. Go and find her a suitable match."

Think a Little Deeper

This story is a *mashal* for the way Hashem sometimes deals with us. He sets up situations that prepare us for difficult times. When you sense discomfort in your life, try to reframe and see it as a source of blessing for the future.

40
THE SMALL STUFF

*I*saac was under a lot of pressure. It was an extra-inning baseball play-off game and he was up at bat. The outcome of the game depended on this play. The air was thick with tension as Isaac closed his eyes and crouched into position. The ball came fast and *thwack,* Isaac made a perfect hit.

Everyone cheered as Isaac ran around the bases.

After the game, friends and teammates surrounded Isaac.

"How did you come through with the winning hit under so much pressure?" they asked.

"Before I stepped up to the plate," he said, "I prayed to Hashem to help me."

"What?" another player replied, incredulous. "You wasted your prayers on that? There are so many more important things to pray for in life. Don't waste your *tefillos* on pettiness."

"I disagree," said another. "Everything that happens is from Hashem. Hashem is just as involved in our baseball games as He is in the big things, like health and livelihood. We are His children and He always wants to hear from us."

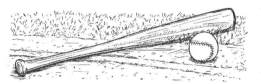

Let's Talk About It

Nobody loves you more than Hashem. He cares about every detail of your life. Can you think of something "small" you want to pray for?

See page 244 for possible answers.

Think a Little Deeper

How does praying for "small stuff" demonstrate our *emunah* in Hashem?

See page 244 for possible answers.

Great People, Great *Emunah*

A grandson of the Steipler Gaon once mentioned to his grandfather that he was going to the Kosel. The great sage requested, "Please mention my name in your prayers."

The grandson was astonished. "But you are so much closer to Hashem than I am!"

"Please listen carefully," the great Gaon said. It says the Midrash, "אֵין שׁוּם תְּפִלָּה חוֹזֶרֶת רֵיקָם — No prayer ever goes unanswered."

It's a fact of creation. Every single word of prayer that leaves the mouth of a Jew is gathered up by Hashem. Every *tefillah* accomplishes something. We might not see the results today or tomorrow; it could even take 100 years. But results are always produced.

41
A RANDOM SPILL

Leeba Segal's mother was an author. She had a special studio in the back of the house where she wrote storybooks for children.

One afternoon, Leeba invited her friend Bracha to come over and spend time together. They played games, went outside, and shared a snack.

"What else can we do?" Bracha wondered aloud.

"Would you like to see my mother's studio?" Leeba offered.

"Oh, yes!" Bracha's face lit up. Mrs. Segal was famous and Bracha was thrilled to see her work area.

The two girls approached the writing studio. "My mother allows us to look around as long as we don't touch anything," Leeba said.

They entered the room and Bracha looked around in wonder. There were notebooks everywhere and bookshelves lined the room. In the center was a large writing desk. The desk had all kinds of interesting writing materials on it. There were markers, fountain pens, gel pens, and of course, regular pens and pencils.

"Most of my mother's work ends up being typed on the computer, but she likes to start out with pen and paper," Leeba explained. "My mother's pretty artistic too. Sometimes she sketches drawings with notations for the illustrator."

Bracha was fascinated. "Hey, what's this?" she asked. She leaned over the desk where a crisp white paper rested. Straight lines of handwritten words were penned neatly across it. "This looks like a great story!"

"That's actually a brand new manuscript," said a voice from the doorway. Both girls whirled around. It was the author herself.

"I was just admiring the story on the desk," Bracha said shyly. "It's so realistic."

Mrs. Segal smiled. "Actually, that's not my work. That story simply wrote itself. Last night, when I finished up in the studio, I prepared a blank sheet of paper for today. I accidentally left one of the inkwells uncovered. It seems like the ink spilled out onto the paper and formed these wonderful words."

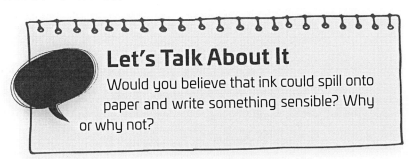

Let's Talk About It

Would you believe that ink could spill onto paper and write something sensible? Why or why not?

See page 244 for possible answers.

"Mommy, that never happened before!" Leeba exclaimed. "When you write a story, you think about every single word! It takes a long time, and you make sure the words make perfect sense. How could this perfect handwriting and wonderful story happen from a random spill?"

"My dears," Mrs. Segal said, "you are right. I actually wrote this story early this morning. The words you see did not happen from a 'random spill.' Nothing in the world happens randomly. If you think about our wonderful bodies, even the tiniest parts like eyelashes, which protect our eyes by keeping out dust and dirt, you will recognize that everything was designed and created by Hashem."

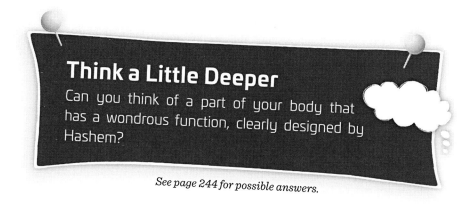

Think a Little Deeper
Can you think of a part of your body that has a wondrous function, clearly designed by Hashem?

See page 244 for possible answers.

42
READY AND WAITING

Akiva was marrying off his daughter. He should have been filled with happiness, but one thought weighed him down. How would he pay for the wedding?

He did not have wealthy family members or friends who could help him out. With no other place to turn, he approached the local yeshivah. He spoke with the man in charge of finances and explained his situation.

"Would you share with me a list of some of your big donors?" he asked. "Perhaps they can help me out."

The administrator was apologetic. "It is against yeshivah policy to share such information," he said. "However, I can give you one name. There's a fellow who donates an average of $26 a year. I don't think he'll mind."

Akiva left with a small piece of paper with the address and phone number of Joseph Goldberg. He realized that his chances of getting a lot of money from him were slim.

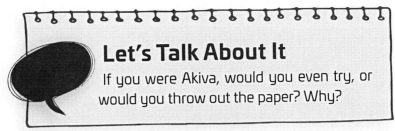

Let's Talk About It

If you were Akiva, would you even try, or would you throw out the paper? Why?

See page 245 for possible answers.

A short while later, a joyful Akiva called the yeshivah.

"I want to thank you for leading me to Mr. Goldberg," he said to the administrator. "He gave me enough money to cover all my wedding expenses."

The administrator was mystified. Mr. Goldberg had never made such a large donation. What was going on? He decided to ask the man directly.

Mr. Goldberg explained that he was in need of a *yeshuah*. As an extra merit, he pledged to Hashem that he would help the next person who approaches him for charity and give him everything he needs.

Akiva approached him at exactly the right time.

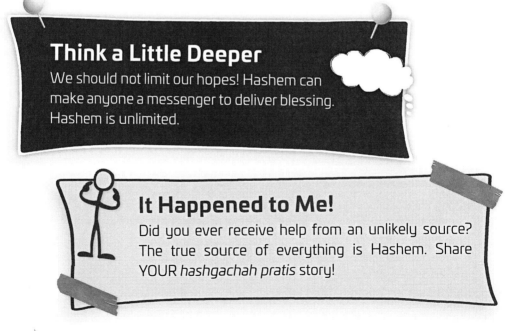

Think a Little Deeper

We should not limit our hopes! Hashem can make anyone a messenger to deliver blessing. Hashem is unlimited.

It Happened to Me!

Did you ever receive help from an unlikely source? The true source of everything is Hashem. Share YOUR *hashgachah pratis* story!

43
A COUPLE OF CUPS

*U*ri was known as the Cup Man. He operated a small company that packaged and sold disposable cups. Business was okay, but the Cup Man was not satisfied. He tried thinking of ways to turn a bigger profit.

One day, a shady idea crept into his mind. Each package was supposed to contain 150 cups. *I can put in 149 and no one will ever know,* he thought. Uri knew it wasn't honest, but he couldn't resist the temptation. The very next day, he implemented his new plan.

Sure enough, the company's earnings increased. The Cup Man was pleased, but unfortunately, he became even greedier. He lowered the amount of cups per package to 148.

As you might have guessed, he was soon selling packs of 147 cups, and then 146. The package labels remained the same, telling customers that they contained 150 cups. Eventually, Uri went down to 142 cups per package.

Let's Talk About It
How does *emunah* keep us honest in business?

See page 245 for possible answers.

Meanwhile, in his personal life, Uri was making changes. He started learning Torah with a religious man and gradually became more observant. As he learned more practical halachah, Uri realized how terrible his thievery was. He felt terrible about it and wanted to do *teshuvah*.

Uri told his story to Rav Elyashiv and asked the great *posek* for guidance. Rav Elyashiv instructed him to pay back the public by adding eight extra cups per package, totaling 158.

This was not easy for the Cup Man. He had watched his business grow since lessening the amount of cups in each package. Now he would take a big hit. Nevertheless, he followed Rav Elyashiv's instructions.

It didn't take long for the company's profits to be affected. The Cup Man was definitely losing money. Still, he stayed strong and didn't budge.

One day, a feature article was published in the newspaper. It was all about the disposable cup market. The newspaper printed a list of companies who cheated their customers by including fewer cups than the package listed. Then the article announced, "There is one company that actually puts eight extra cups in every package. They are very reputable, and we recommend supporting them by purchasing their products."

This was a turning point for Uri's company. Orders skyrocketed, and he needed a bigger warehouse. He expanded his business to include disposable plates, forks, and knives.

Uri the Cup Man had built himself a reputation as an honest man, and Hashem blessed him with long-lasting financial success.

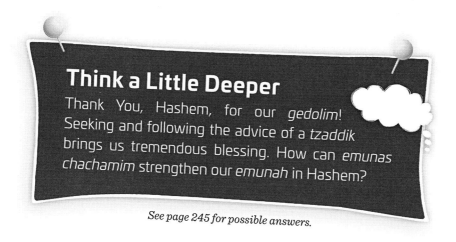

Think a Little Deeper

Thank You, Hashem, for our *gedolim!* Seeking and following the advice of a *tzaddik* brings us tremendous blessing. How can *emunas chachamim* strengthen our *emunah* in Hashem?

See page 245 for possible answers.

44
DO YOU BELIEVE?

Rabbi Menachem Mendel Futerfas was imprisoned in Siberia for eight years. It was a time filled with terrible suffering, yet he always believed that Hashem would release him. When he was eventually freed, he was asked how he managed to remain strong in his *emunah* for so long.

He replied with a story that he had witnessed one day in Siberia.

During a short break, one inmate asked the rest of us if we wanted to watch him walk a tightrope between two mountains. We all said no, because we were too afraid for his safety. The man was stubborn and did it anyway. As he slowly walked across the rope, we were afraid to even look. Finally he made it to the other side. He called out to us, asking if we wanted to see how he walked back. Again, we all said no, but he did it anyway.

We thought he was done performing but the man was not satisfied with his antics. Now he announced that he would walk the tightrope with a wagon attached to himself. We watched with bated breath as he completed this fantastic feat. This time, when the man said he would cross back the same way, we knew he would do it anyway. So we all said, "You have al-

ready proven yourself. We know you can easily walk back on the tightrope, even attached to a wagon." The man called back, "Do you really believe I can?" We all responded, "Yes, we really believe!" The man then challenged us by offering, "If you really believe, which one of you is willing to sit in the wagon as I wheel it across?" Nobody budged.

Let's Talk About It

The onlookers all told the tightrope walker that they believed he could successfully cross the rope with a wagon. Yet nobody was willing to sit in it. What does this tell us about the level of their belief in the tightrope walker?

See page 245 for possible answers.

None of us volunteered to sit in the wagon. "I see you don't fully believe in my abilities," concluded the tightrope walker.

Rabbi Futerfas used this story as a measuring stick for his own belief in Hashem. "Ever since that day, I've been asking myself, could I sit calmly in a wagon if I knew it was controlled by Hashem? Could I envision myself in His capable hands and place my full trust in Him? With this mind-set, I realized that even in Siberia, there is nothing to fear."

David HaMelech wrote in *Tehillim,* גַּם כִּי אֵלֵךְ בְּגֵיא צַלְמָוֶת לֹא אִירָא רָע כִּי אַתָּה עִמָּדִי — "Even as I walk through the valley of death, I will not fear evil because You, Hashem, are with me."

Think a Little Deeper

How can we apply the lesson from this story to our relationship with Hashem?

See page 245 for possible answers.

45
LAST MINUTE

hen Avraham Avinu was about to slaughter his son Yitzchak, they were both prepared to carry through the will of Hashem. However, at the last moment, Hashem called out and stopped them.

Some years down the line, when the Jewish people were leaving Egypt, they stood before the mighty *yam suf*. Only when the water reached the nostrils of Nachshon ben Aminadav did Hashem perform the incredible miracle of splitting the sea.

In both of these landmark moments in Jewish history, Hashem waited until the last possible moment to save His beloved children. Why so?

Hashem knows the precise timings of everything that occurs. He does not need to prepare in advance to ensure success. Human beings obviously do not have that ability. If we have an appointment, we need to plan in order to arrive in time.

Why would Hashem wait until the last minute? Here are several possible reasons.

1. As we wait, we pray to Hashem and come closer to Him.
2. During the waiting period, we practice our *emunah* by relying on Hashem instead of worrying.
3. The prayer and *emunah* we display while waiting can be the final *zechus* needed in order to bring the salvation.
4. We use the time to do *hishtadlus* and invest appropriate efforts to help the situation.
5. We work on seeing the good, even in the present "imperfect" situation.
6. The discomfort we endure while we wait for salvation purifies us and serves as a *kapparah*.
7. We learn that salvation can always come, even at the last second.
8. Once the *yeshuah* arrives, we appreciate it so much more.

In the times of the Beis HaMikdash, the Jewish people would travel up to Yerushalayim for the *shalosh regalim*. On one occasion, there was a drought and all of the wells dried up.

A Jew named Nakdimon ben Gurion approached a wealthy landowner to borrow twelve wells of water. He promised that the wells would be refilled by a certain date. Otherwise, he agreed to pay an enormous sum of money instead.

The landowner agreed and the Jewish people were able to drink.

Soon the date of payment arrived and it still had not rained. The twelve wells were due to be returned but they were empty. The wealthy man sent a messenger to collect money from Nakdimon ben Gurion.

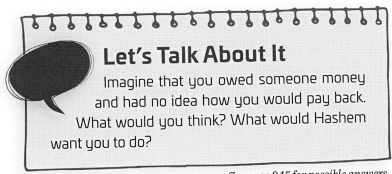

Let's Talk About It
Imagine that you owed someone money and had no idea how you would pay back. What would you think? What would Hashem want you to do?

See page 245 for possible answers.

"I still have an entire day," Nakdimon replied. The wealthy man sent him two more messages and both times Nakdimon answered, "There is still time."

Meanwhile, the hours continued to pass and there was not a cloud in the sky. Nakdimon went into the *Beis HaMikdash* and prayed to Hashem for a salvation. Immediately, the sky filled with rain clouds and in a very short time, every single well was filled to capacity.

This occurred in the final second of that day.

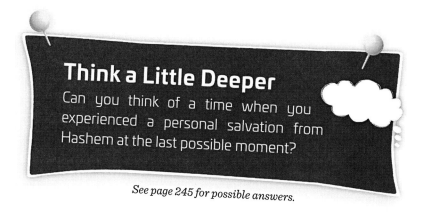

Think a Little Deeper

Can you think of a time when you experienced a personal salvation from Hashem at the last possible moment?

See page 245 for possible answers.

46
CHEW IT OVER

We all need food. Food gives us energy to perform our daily tasks. In order to be absorbed by the body, food must be broken down. This process starts in the mouth, where your teeth play a big role.

Your teeth are definitely equipped for the job. They are covered with shiny white enamel. Enamel is the hardest substance in your body, even stronger than bone.

Hashem blessed us with specially designed teeth. Each type of tooth is shaped differently and has a distinct job. As a team, they work together to efficiently cut, tear, crush, and grind food so that it fits through the throat for the rest of its journey.

At the very front of the mouth are your incisors, shaped like tiny chisels. They have flat ends that are somewhat sharp. They are ideally designed to cut into and chop food.

Four canine teeth surround the incisors; two on top and two on bottom. They are also sharp but more pointed than incisors. They help tear food.

Next in line are the premolars. They are further back in the mouth and have a completely different shape. They are bigger and stronger, and their function is to crush and grind food.

At the back of the mouth are molars and wisdom teeth. They are the widest and strongest teeth in the mouth. After food has been cut, torn, and crushed by the rest of the teeth, the tongue sweeps it all to the back where molars mash it up one final time.

Now the food is finally ready to be swallowed.

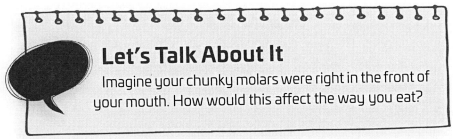

Let's Talk About It

Imagine your chunky molars were right in the front of your mouth. How would this affect the way you eat?

See page 245 for possible answers.

You may think your teeth are only for chewing, but they play an important role in speech as well. Your teeth, tongue, and lips team up to help you form different sounds. Try saying the word "tooth" slowly. Notice the way your tongue hits the inside of your incisors to produce the "t" sound, and then goes between the upper and lower teeth to make the "th" sound. How amazing!

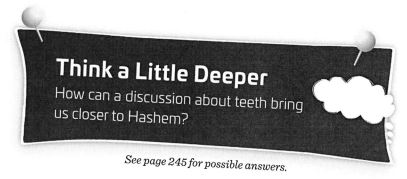

Think a Little Deeper

How can a discussion about teeth bring us closer to Hashem?

See page 245 for possible answers.

47
TWO LUCKY WINNERS

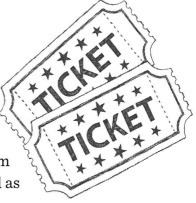

*I*t was the morning of the annual mother-daughter breakfast. The girls were very excited. There would be a performance, breakfast, speeches, and a grand raffle.

At the appointed time, mothers started streaming in. The girls marched onto the stage and performed beautifully. Then they eagerly joined their mothers at the tables.

While the crowd ate, the principal got up to introduce the first speaker, a fourth grader named Chaya Stein.

"Welcome all mothers, and thank you for joining us this morning," she began. Chaya delivered a nice *dvar Torah* and everyone applauded.

The next speaker was Hindy Gross, also from the fourth grade. She spoke with confidence, and as she returned to her seat, everyone clapped.

It was now time to wrap up the event. The grand raffle included second, third, and fourth graders. Only two winners would be chosen.

The principal pulled out the first ticket, which read *Devorah Stein*. Devorah was Chaya's younger sister.

"Our first winner is the sister of one of today's speakers," she announced dramatically. As soon as the words left her mouth, the principal realized that the other speaker, Hindy, also had a younger sister. She was sure the little girl was hoping to win and felt bad to let her hopes down. The principal quickly presented the prize to Devorah and proceeded to draw the next ticket.

"Our next winner is..." The principal paused to read the ticket. To her amazement, the second winner was Malka Gross, Hindy's younger sister!

"Our next winner is also the sister of one of today's speakers. Malka Gross, please come up!" Everyone cheered as Malka ran up to receive her prize.

Let's Talk About It

What can we learn from the fact that Hashem arranged for the second sister to win also?

See page 245 for possible answers.

Think a Little Deeper

Winning a raffle can easily be brushed off as "coincidence." But even "random" raffles are set up and managed by Hashem.

It Happened to Me!

Did you ever experience *hashgachah pratis* at the very last minute? Describe how you felt Hashem's involvement.

48
BIG DEAL

r. Mandel had recently purchased a very beautiful new house. A man of means, he threw a massive party and invited the whole community.

Yechiel and Nosson showed up at the same time. There was a live band, special lighting, and unlimited food. They walked around the room, taking it all in.

"Wow," Yechiel said. "Look at that smoothie station! I really like smoothies. It's so nice of Mr. Mandel to invite us and prepare all these delicious foods."

"Nah," Nosson said with a wave of his hand. "It's no big deal. He was preparing all this anyway. He didn't do anything for me or you personally."

Let's Talk About It

What is wrong with such an attitude?

See page 246 for possible answers.

Think a Little Deeper

The Gemara teaches us to have the feeling of — כָּל שֶׁטָּרַח בַּעַל הַבַּיִת בִּשְׁבִילִי טָרַח "Everything Hashem did, He did for me." When a person walks outside on a beautiful sunny day, he should say, "What a gorgeous day! Thank You, Hashem, for shining Your golden sun especially for me!"

Great People, Great *Emunah*

There was a Yid who was married for a year and was blessed with a baby girl. He came to Rav Shach and asked him if he needed to make a *kiddush*. Rav Shach asked him, "If this child had been born to you after eight years of waiting, would you make a *kiddush*?"

"Of course," the man replied. "What a *simchah* that would be!"

Rav Shach told him, "Hashem was so kind to you, He spared you eight years of waiting. Does that deserve any less of a celebration and *hakaras hatov* to Him?"

49
TODAY IS THE DAY

Yitzchak and Adina were married for a few years. All was well, except they were not blessed with children. Adina became very sad. She would mope around, feeling bad for herself.

This went on for a while, until her husband said, "We have to figure out a way to be happier. Hashem does not want to see us depressed all the time. Hashem is kind."

He took out a calendar and circled the date. "Today is a day of celebration because today is the day we are changing our attitudes."

Together, the couple strengthened themselves and focused on finding the positive in their lives. They truly became happier people.

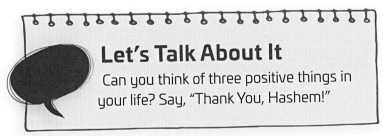

Let's Talk About It
Can you think of three positive things in your life? Say, "Thank You, Hashem!"

See page 246 for possible answers.

Exactly one year after their commitment to change, they were blessed with their first baby. They continued to have a total of five children; four of them were born on that very same special date, the day that they marked as a day of celebration.

Think a Little Deeper

Sometimes we think we need the reality to change in order for us to be happy. If we work on being happy, we may see our reality change.

Let's Reframe With *Emunah* Glasses

Picture this scenario:

You have been looking forward to a class trip for months. The day arrives and the sky is gray. Rain is coming down hard and it doesn't seem to be ending soon. Your class will only be able to experience the indoor parts of the trip, and the ball game you envisioned is not going to happen.

Think: How can I reframe and focus on the good?

50
WHATEVER THE WEATHER

Menashe stepped into his Rabbi's study. He was about to enter the business world for the first time and had come to receive the Rabbi's blessing.

The Rabbi spoke with him warmly and advised, "Accept upon yourself that no matter what, you will never miss praying with a *minyan*."

At first, this was easy for Menashe. The hours of his job allowed him to pray in shul three times a day.

Eventually though, the nature of the business changed. Menashe found himself flying around the world. He returned to his Rabbi and told him it was getting more difficult to find *minyanim*.

"When the mitzvah is harder, it is even more precious," the Rabbi said. "Stick to your commitment and it will bring you blessing."

These words strengthened Menashe's resolve, and sure enough, his business expanded and he became very successful.

On one occasion, Menashe was on a flight that had a stopover scheduled at the JFK airport in New York.

As soon as we land, I will take a cab to a shul, he planned. He figured he could make it back to the airport for his connecting flight.

However, a snowstorm hit the New York area and the flight was delayed. There would not be enough time to travel to a shul.

Let's Talk About It

Picture yourself in this situation. Think:
What would Hashem want me to do?

See page 246 for possible answers.

Menashe was determined not to miss praying with a *minyan.* He contacted a yeshivah in New York and asked the Rosh Yeshivah if he could please send nine boys to meet him in the airport. He was willing to pay each student a lot of money for coming.

Just when Menashe thought he had everything arranged, the pilot announced that due to the storm, they were going to have to land somewhere else.

Now he was really disappointed. Nine boys would come from the yeshivah and he would not even be there to pray with them. How would he ever find a *minyan*?

He went up down the aisles of the plane, searching for Jews. There were only two others. He sat back down, opened a *Tehillim* and started to cry.

Hashem, he pleaded, *I have tried everything in my power. Please give me the merit to pray with a minyan.*

Just then, the loudspeaker came on. "Attention all passengers, this is your pilot speaking."

Menashe sat up straight in his seat. He didn't want to miss a word of this announcement.

"We just received notice that we will be able to land in JFK after all," the pilot said.

Menashe breathed a sigh of relief.

But there was still another surprise waiting for him. Upon arrival, he looked around for the yeshivah boys, but they were nowhere to be found. He contacted the Rosh Yeshivah, who apologized and said the roads were too unsafe for the students to drive over.

Before he could think about what to do next, Menashe looked up and saw fifty Jews walking toward him. They had been on another plane that had landed in JFK because of the snowstorm.

After a long, stressful day, Menashe's face finally broke into a smile as he joined his Jewish brothers and prayed to Hashem.

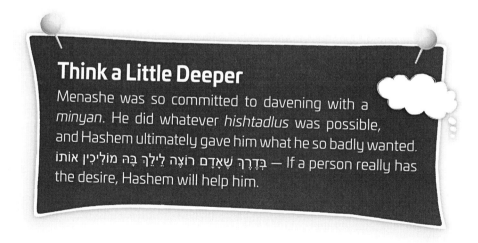

Think a Little Deeper

Menashe was so committed to davening with a minyan. He did whatever *hishtadlus* was possible, and Hashem ultimately gave him what he so badly wanted. בְּדֶרֶךְ שֶׁאָדָם רוֹצֶה לֵילֵךְ בָּהּ מוֹלִיכִין אוֹתוֹ — If a person really has the desire, Hashem will help him.

51
TAKE A
DEEP BREATH

*T*ake a deep breath... Air! What would we do without it?

Planet Earth is surrounded by a blanket of air called the atmosphere. Hashem created the atmosphere with a perfect balance of nitrogen, oxygen, argon, carbon dioxide, and other gases. Too much or too little of these gases would be toxic.

One of the great wonders of the atmosphere is the way it absorbs harmful sunrays. It traps ultraviolet radiation and blocks it from reaching humans, animals, and plants.

The atmosphere also traps heat from the sun. This keeps us warm overnight when the sun is not there.

The air we have on Earth does not exist on the moon, nor on any other planet. When astronauts leave Earth's atmosphere and enter space, they need to be attached to special breathing machines that provide them with air.

Let's Talk About It

Only the air on planet Earth is healthy for people, animals, and plants. Who can determine such a perfect formula? It can only be Hashem!

See page 246 for possible answers.

Think a Little Deeper

Can you think of something else in nature that we need in order to exist? Say, "Thank You, Hashem!"

Great People, Great *Emunah*

Rav Avigdor Miller was well known for valuing Hashem's wonders, down to the smallest things.

Once, a grandchild visited Rav Miller's home. He was surprised to find his grandfather leaning over the sink, his face submerged in water. After a few moments, Rav Miller stood up and breathed deeply.

"The air is so wonderful," he said.

Now the grandchild was really puzzled.

Rav Miller explained, "Earlier, I heard someone comment about the level of pollution in the air. I didn't want my appreciation of Hashem's air to lessen, so I deprived myself of it for just a short while."

"Now I am even more thankful than before," Rav Miller concluded.

52
HOT WATER

Rabbi Kalman Greenwald had an aunt who passed away childless. He wanted to do something in her merit. He decided to donate a hot water urn to Kever Rachel. *Berachos* that would be recited over hot drinks would serve as a merit for his aunt. He purchased an urn and placed a sign upon it that read, *"L'iluy nishmas* Dina bas Yehudah."

Over time, the urn was used by many Jews who came to pray at the *kever.* Eventually, though, it was replaced by a newer and larger one. The new system connected directly to the water pipes and did not need to be refilled. The one donated by Rabbi Greenwald was put into storage.

One year, on the 23rd day of Shevat, the new water system stopped working. It was close to evening and nobody could get it to start again.

Let's Talk About It
Imagine it was your job to provide hot water at Kever Rachel. One day, the urn breaks down. How would Hashem want you to react?

See page 246 for possible answers.

The people in charge of upkeep at the *kever* looked around for a temporary solution. They found four urns in storage. The one that was selected was the one donated *l'iluy nishmas* Dina bas Yehudah. That night and the entire next day, the urn donated by Rabbi Greenwald was used by Jews visiting Kever Rachel.

The day after that, a handyman came to fix the newer, larger urn. Strangely, all he had to do to get it working again was plug a wire into the wall. The management team wondered how they had all missed such a simple solution.

"It's not as strange as it seems," one of the workers said. "The 24th day of Shevat is the *yahrtzeit* of Dina bas Yehudah. It seems that the urn that was dedicated in her merit was meant to be used on that specific day."

Think a Little Deeper
How do stories of *hashgachah pratis* like this one help strengthen our *emunah*?

See page 246 for possible answers.

It Happened to Me!
Did you ever wonder why something "bad" happened to you? Did you merit to see how it was really for the good? Share YOUR *hashgachah pratis* story!

53
CHASING THE MOON

*I*t was Motzaei Yom Kippur. Amram had just finished eating the post-fast meal when he received a phone call from his Rabbi.

"I have an interesting favor to ask you," the Rabbi said. "A man is flying in from Detroit, Michigan, to say *kiddush levanah*. The weather forecast for Detroit is four days of rain, and this fellow is coming out here to Atlanta, Georgia, because he heard that we have clear skies."

Amram was floored. He knew that the halachah states that if the moon is blocked by clouds, one is exempt from making the *berachah*. And here was a man who was willing to get onto a plane just to be able to bless the new moon? Incredible.

"How can I help this special person?" he asked.

"Well," the Rabbi answered, "he asked if I could arrange for a *minyan* to meet him at the airport so that he can make the *berachah* in the best possible manner."

Although the hour was late and Amram was exhausted from having fasted all day, he agreed to drive down to the airport. There he met the man from Detroit, whose name was Moti Weisberg. They blessed the moon with much joy and Moti took a flight back soon after. Amram knew this was a story he would never forget.

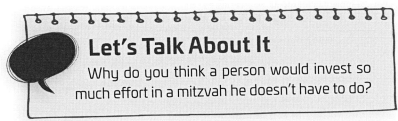

Let's Talk About It

Why do you think a person would invest so much effort in a mitzvah he doesn't have to do?

See page 246 for possible answers.

About fifteen years later, when he was living in Lakewood, New Jersey, Amram found himself driving along the New Jersey Turnpike on the way home from a wedding. He stopped off at a rest area. There he saw a most amazing sight: several Jewish men stood together with siddurim in their hands, saying *kiddush levanah*! Pulled toward the beauty of the scene, he approached the group.

"Why are you saying *kiddush levanah* here, at the side of the road?" he asked curiously.

"It's been raining in Lakewood for days," they said. "We decided to drive as far as we needed to catch the moon. This is where we found it."

Amram was impressed. He told the boys the remarkable story of the time Moti Weisberg flew from Detroit to Atlanta in order to catch a clear moon.

One man in the group started smiling. He pointed to another man and said, "Allow me to introduce you to Daniel Weisberg, Moti Weisberg's son."

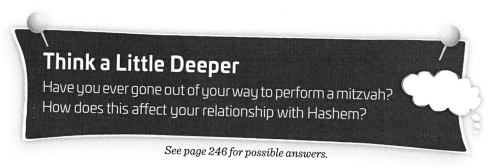

Think a Little Deeper

Have you ever gone out of your way to perform a mitzvah? How does this affect your relationship with Hashem?

See page 246 for possible answers.

54
SIX PRECIOUS MONTHS

*A*ll eyes were glued to Rabbi Balk as he delivered a fiery speech. He had traveled to the United States to fundraise for yeshivos in Eretz Yisrael. This Shabbos, he was in Chicago. Rabbi Balk passionately described the beauty of Yerushalayim and its *talmidei chachamim*. The crowd hung on to every word.

After Shabbos, many community members rushed to bring donations to the Rabbi. They all wanted the *zechus* of supporting Torah learning. One man, Mr. Yerachmiel Wexler, seemed more inspired than the rest.

"Rabbi Balk," he said, "your words are very moving. I want to have a part in the Torah learning you describe. Not only will I hand you a donation, I am considering moving to Eretz Yisrael and setting up a business there. I want to support the Jews of Yerushalayim on a regular basis."

Mr. Wexler was a man who meant what he said. Together with his son Yechezkel, he made the trip to Eretz Yisrael. His first stop was at the Chevron Yeshivah. Father and son met the young men who learned there, including several American boys. They were both very impressed by what they saw, and Mr. Wexler wanted his son to be a part of it. And so, even though Yechezkel did not have a strong yeshivah background, he enrolled in the Chevron Yeshivah. His father returned to America.

That winter, Yechezkel Wexler learned like never before. He flourished in his new environment. But after only half a year, tragedy struck. The local Arabs massacred many Jews in Chevron and Yechezkel was one of the victims. Back in Chicago, his parents sat *shivah* and mourned the loss of their beloved son.

Sometime later, Rabbi Balk was again asked to sail to the United States to raise funds.

"I agree to go," he said. "But I cannot visit Chicago. I cannot face Mr. Wexler after what happened to his son." He felt terrible for having indirectly led Yechezkel to his tragic fate.

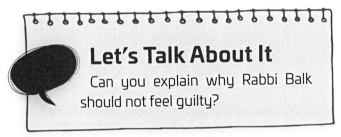

Let's Talk About It
Can you explain why Rabbi Balk should not feel guilty?

See page 246 for possible answers.

Once again, Rabbi Balk traveled to America. He delivered dynamic speeches throughout New York. One day, as he walked toward the place he was staying, he bumped into none other than Mr. Wexler.

"*Shalom aleichem*, Reb Yerachmiel," he said a bit nervously.

Mr. Wexler warmly embraced the Rabbi.

"Rabbi Balk," he exclaimed, "it is wonderful to see you! I was wondering why you didn't come to Chicago."

Now the Rabbi was even more uncomfortable. "W-w-well," he stammered, "I've been avoiding Chicago because I feel terrible about having caused you to lose your son."

"Lose my son?!" Mr. Wexler cried out. "You *gave* me my son! His soul was destined to be on this earth for twenty years. This was his time to go. If you had not come to Chicago, he probably would have gone to the Next World without knowing as much Torah. But because of you, he was immersed in Hashem's Torah for six months. Thank you, Rabbi Balk. You gave my son *Olam Haba!*"

Think a Little Deeper

Mr. Wexler spoke with amazing *emunah*. He truly felt that כָּל מַה דְּעָבִיד רַחֲמָנָא לְטָבָא עָבִיד, to the point that he was able to express gratitude toward Rabbi Balk for his role in Yechezkel's transfer to Eretz Yisrael.

55
GARDEN OF MIRACLES

The Lev family's vegetable patch was a year-round project. During the fall, they saved their vegetable peels and eggshells for natural compost. Right before winter, they used the compost to fertilize the soil in their backyard. And finally, in early spring, they planted seeds.

They planted tomatoes, cucumbers, radishes, carrots, squash, and sugar snap peas.

Every morning, Henny and Faigy ran straight to the backyard to check on their garden. They would carefully remove weeds and search the ground for fresh sprouts. For the first few days, they found no sign of vegetables. Still, they watered the earth and prayed, "Please, Hashem, help our vegetables grow."

Let's Talk About It

Do you think the garden would grow even if the children wouldn't pray to Hashem? What is the purpose of their prayers?

See page 247 for possible answers.

One magical day, a tiny green leaf poked out of the ground.

"The cucumbers are here!" the kids shouted with joy.

"It takes a while until the vegetables grow," their mother cautioned. "Now our job is to keep watering the little sprouts so they grow healthy and strong."

The next day, the squash leaves poked through the earth. And nearly every day after that, another vegetable plant made its appearance. Soon the yard was full of greenery, and Henny and Faigy learned to tell the plants apart according to their leaves. Some plants even grew flowers.

"Now that the flowers are coming in, the bees will do their job," Mommy told her daughters.

"Bees? Why do we need bees?" Henny asked. "We plant seeds, Hashem sends rain, and we pull out the weeds; why do our plants need bees?"

"Our plants will only grow vegetables if their flowers are pollinated," their mother explained. "Plants and trees are stuck in the ground and cannot spread pollen on their own. They depend on flying insects such as bees to pollinate them."

The kids listened as they pulled weeds from the earth. "Bees fly from flower to flower. You can actually see one right there." Their mother pointed to a bright yellow flower attached to a cucumber plant. A honey bee crawled along the petals, deep into the center of the flower.

"This honey bee flew here to drink nectar from the flower. It will use the nectar to make honey. But while it is in the flower, crumbs of pollen are sticking to tiny hairs on its body." Just then, the bee flew off to another flower in the garden. "Now the bee is carrying the pollen crumbs to the next flower. This is called pollination, and it helps the plants grow vegetables."

"Do you know what other wonderful things a bee can do?"

"They make honey!" Faigy said.

"That's right. Bees make honey, and beeswax too. People can then eat the honey and use the beeswax to make candles."

The children looked around at the garden of miracles surrounding them.

"What's the most important part of planting?" their mother asked with a smile.

Together, the sisters sang out, "Thank You, Hashem, for our wonderful vegetable patch, and please Hashem, help everything grow well!"

Think a Little Deeper
What do the children gain by constantly realizing and noticing Hashem's involvement in their planting process?

See page 247 for possible answers.

56
THE NOSE KNOWS

Something smelled burnt. Mrs. Wilner rushed to the kitchen to check it out. A black slice of pizza sat smoking in the toaster.

"Bentzi," she called out to her twelve-year-old son, "your lunch is burning!"

Your nose gives you valuable information about the environment. It also plays a major role in breathing. What would we do without this wonderful gift?

Here are some facts to help you appreciate your miraculous nose.

Your nose can tell apart more than one trillion different scents. This puts it way ahead of your eyes and ears, which can discriminate between several million colors and about half a million tones.

Our sense of smell lets us know if food is safe to eat. It alerts us about food that is undercooked or spoiled.

The nose is the main entrance for air that enters the body.

Blood vessels along the nasal passage warm the air traveling to the lungs.

When the nasal passage becomes overloaded with dust, an automatic system triggers a sneeze that gets rid of unwanted particles — what a miracle!

Let's Talk About It

Many scents exist solely for our pleasure. What does this tell us about Hashem's love for us?

See page 247 for possible answers.

Think a Little Deeper

How does studying the wonders in your nose bring you closer to Hashem?

See page 247 for possible answers.

Great People, Great *Emunah*

In the *Modim* prayer, we thank Hashem for everything He does for us. The root word for הוֹדָאָה, which means *thanks*, appears twice in the same paragraph. Why isn't once enough?

Rav Chaim Kanievsky explains that first we thank Hashem for everything He has done for us until today. The second thank You is for everything Hashem is going to do for us in the future.

We have so much to be thankful for!

57
CIRCLE OF KINDNESS

*I*t was Friday morning, and Avigdor Aranson wanted to buy food for Shabbos. He knew he was going to get a lot of money on Sunday, but right now, his wallet was empty.

He tried to think of whom he could ask for a short-term loan. Should he try someone from shul? There was one man who seemed nice. He didn't look like a man of means, and Avigdor didn't even know his name. Still, he was friendly and easygoing and Avigdor felt comfortable approaching him.

Right after Shacharis, Avigdor went over to him. He explained that he needed some cash for a couple of days. The man happily agreed and handed over a pile of bills. Avigdor wrote up a document that said, "Avigdor Aronson will give you x amount of money on Sunday." With a bounce in his step, he went out to buy food for Shabbos.

On Sunday, as promised, he returned

the money to the kind man in shul.

"Oh, wow," the man gushed. "*Baruch Hashem*! Thank you for paying me back!"

Avigdor wasn't sure why he was so appreciative.

The man saw Avigdor's surprise and explained, "I always keep my money in a little pouch. On Friday, it was filled with cash for the entire month. After you and I spoke, I took a bus somewhere and accidentally left my pouch on the seat. I was so distraught. But fortunately, half the money was by you, and now you are returning it to me."

Let's Talk About It

Did you ever give something to another person? Were you able to see how you were actually helping yourself by doing *chesed*?

See page 247 for possible answers.

Later that day, Avigdor received a phone call from a number he didn't recognize.

"Did you lose a money pouch?" the caller asked. "I found a pouch with money and an IOU note signed by Avigdor Aronson. I did some research and tracked you down."

Avigdor realized that the rest of the money had been found. He made arrangements to meet the caller and returned the pouch to its grateful lender.

Think a Little Deeper

How can being on the receiving end of *chesed* strengthen our *emunah*?

58
THE GIFT
OF *TESHUVAH*

Teshuvah is one of the greatest gifts Hashem has given us. With a few moments of sincerity, a person can wipe away years of sin.

Daniel and Reuven were best friends. When they were young children, they went to the same school and always played together.

As they grew older, their friendship deepened. They became study partners and learned Torah with zest. The two friends were admired by their Rabbis and peers.

After high school, things took an unfortunate turn. The two teenagers started to hang out with the wrong crowd. Their new group had a terrible influence on them and over time they strayed from the proper path. The situation deteriorated to the point where they both became public sinners. Their small community was in shock over the extreme turnaround. Some neighbors and friends reached out to the young men but nothing anyone said or did would bring them back. Their parents were terribly heartbroken.

Daniel soon became a successful businessman and married a non-Jewish woman. Reuven moved to a different location and the two friends drifted apart.

Years went by. One morning, Reuven was walking his dog in a forest. The dog ran ahead and stopped at the body of a man at the side of the path. Reuven could tell the man was a religious Jew who appeared to have been murdered. He rushed to a nearby town and told the Rabbi about the Jew in the forest. The man was given a proper burial in a Jewish cemetery.

From that day on, Reuven did not feel peace. He felt terrible that he was so distanced from Judaism, and he wanted to come back to Hashem. He knew he was very far gone, and had neglected Torah and mitzvos for so many years, but he really wanted to return.

Although he did not look Jewish, he gathered the courage to approach a Rabbi.

"I am a Jew," he said. "I want to do *teshuvah*. Please help me."

The Rabbi saw that Reuven was sincere. He guided him back to Judaism and soon Reuven was learning Torah day and night. He continued to grow until he became the Rabbi's top student.

When the Rabbi aged and was no longer able to lead his congregation, he appointed Reuven to take his place.

One day, as Reuven was leading the congregation in shul, a stranger entered the building. He walked straight up to the front and started yelling like a madman.

"This man is a fraud!" he shouted. "He is no Rabbi at all! He did the worst sins with me." Reuven realized that this man was Daniel, his old friend from the past. The man kept screaming, hurling insults and evil words at the Rabbi.

The shul members were stunned. But what happened next surprised them even more.

Reuven, their respected Rabbi, got up and said, "This man is right. He speaks the truth. I was a sinner, but *teshuvah* was created even for people like me. Though I fell very low, I came back to Hashem fully, with all my heart. Hashem forgives the sins of those who repent sincerely."

The man finally finished his rant. Over time, Reuven was able to bring him back to *teshuvah* as well.

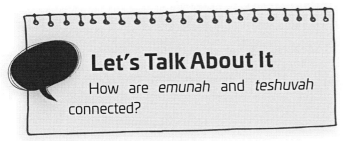

Let's Talk About It

How are *emunah* and *teshuvah* connected?

See page 247 for possible answers.

Great People, Great *Emunah*

When Rav Yosef Kahaneman, the Rosh Yeshivah of Ponevezh, was traveling abroad, he asked the Chafetz Chaim, "What words of wisdom can I bring back with me to my hometown?"

The Chafetz Chaim replied, "Tell the people how easy it is to do *teshuvah*. One only has to feel bad about the past and accept to be better in the future." The holy Chafetz Chaim continued, "People need to know not to fall into the trap of the *yetzer hara* who tries to convince them that *teshuvah* is hard. It's not. *Teshuvah* is simple."

59
A WARM GESTURE

*I*n the world of kosher ice cream, Klein's and Mehadrin are two of the most recognized brands. Both companies maintain huge freezers to store their supply of frozen treats.

One summer, there was a major blackout that affected the East coast. Over fifty million people lost electric power. This was a serious crisis for dairy companies, including Klein's and Mehadrin. Summer is their prime season, and thousands of ice cream buckets, popsicles, and ices began melting in the heat.

Baruch Hashem, after five hours, electricity was restored to the Klein's ice cream facility. But then the Klein brothers found out that their competitor, Mehadrin, would only get their power back after two full days, causing a tremendous loss.

Let's Talk About It

How would you advise Klein's at this point? They have their electricity back, but their competition does not. Would you offer to help them, or would you say, business is business — Mehadrin will just have to take a loss?

See page 247 for possible answers.

The Klein brothers called a quick meeting. "Hashem is in charge of our *parnassah*," they declared. "Now we have an opportunity to help someone in need, and we are going to do it!"

With tremendous *bitachon,* the Klein family contacted the owners of Mehadrin. They invited them to plug their trucks into their warehouse. Klein's and Mehadrin trucks parked side by side in Klein's facility, and Klein's saved the entire inventory of their biggest competitor.

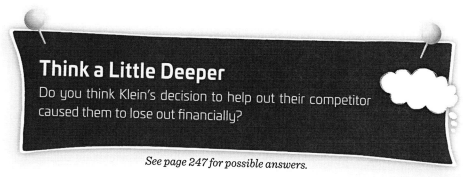

Think a Little Deeper

Do you think Klein's decision to help out their competitor caused them to lose out financially?

See page 247 for possible answers.

The Gemara states, אֵין אָדָם נוֹגֵעַ בַּמּוּכָן לַחֲבֵרוֹ — Nobody can take away what Hashem has set aside for you. You will get every dollar Hashem wants you to have. You need not worry that you will lose out by doing the right thing.

Let's Reframe With *Emunah* Glasses

Picture this scenario:

You are preparing for a schoolwide competition. You have a good chance of winning. Then, the night before the competition, your friend tells you he lost his study sheets and would like a copy of yours.

It would take you two minutes to make a photocopy. But you don't really want to decrease your chances of winning.

Should you help out your friend? Why or why not? How would Hashem want you to react?

60

THE SECRET MITZVAH CHAIN

Mendy peered into his older brother's room to see if it was empty. The coast was clear! He crept in silently, holding one of Chanoch's shoes in each hand. Chanoch was learning Torah downstairs in the study and Mendy had found his shoes under the couch. He knew that Chanoch woke up early for *minyan* and he figured he would help his brother save some time during the morning rush.

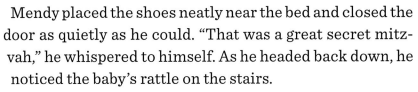

Mendy placed the shoes neatly near the bed and closed the door as quietly as he could. "That was a great secret mitzvah," he whispered to himself. As he headed back down, he noticed the baby's rattle on the stairs.

I should probably move this so nobody trips, he thought. With a smile, Mendy picked up the rattle and put it in the bin with the rest of the baby's toys.

At last, Mendy made it to the kitchen where he prepared

himself a glass of water. He saw that the milk was still on the table. "Wow, a third secret mitzvah!" he said. He put the milk in the refrigerator and smiled again. "I started out by putting away Chanoch's shoes and look how lucky I got!"

Let's Talk About It

How does doing a secret *chesed* show our *emunah*?

See page 248 for possible answers.

Think a Little Deeper

Let's stop and think to ourselves: What secret mitzvah can I do today?

See page 248 for possible answers.

Great People, Great *Emunah*

Rav Avigdor Miller writes in his *Ten Steps to Greatness*, "A person should attempt to do one good deed a day that nobody knows about."

Even a good deed that is "simple" or "small" accomplishes a great deal. Hashem sees it, and it reaffirms our *emunah* in Him. This makes the mitzvah worth so much.

61
CRYSTAL CLEAR

Looking at a glass of water, you might think it is the simplest thing around. Pure water is colorless, odorless, and tasteless.

But water is not as simple as it seems. All life on and inside Earth depends on water. A person can technically survive about a month without food, but only about a week without water. This is because most of your body is water. This is how much water is found in some of your major body parts, according to the research of biologists:

The heart is 73% water.

The brain is 73% water.

The lungs are 83% water.

The skin is 64% water.

The muscles are 79% water.

The kidneys are 79% water.

The bones are 31% water.

Water dissolves more substances than any other

liquid. Wherever it flows, it takes along chemicals, minerals, and nutrients. This helps it transport different materials along the ground, and even inside our bodies!

Water can carry sound for long distances. This helps fish and water creatures hear each other in lakes, rivers, and oceans.

One of the most remarkable things about water is that it is a renewable resource. It moves in a cycle, evaporating and forming clouds, coming back down as rain, sleet, or snow, and then evaporating again. In this way, humans, animals, and plants have access to the water they need.

Let's Talk About It

Rain comes directly from Hashem, with no middleman. This makes it easier for us to see how dependent we are on Hashem for rain. What are some ways you can thank Hashem for water?

See page 248 for possible answers.

Think a Little Deeper

What a beautiful perspective! Can you think of a benefit of water being tasteless?

See page 248 for possible answers.

Great People, Great *Emunah*

Rav Avigdor Miller points out the benefit of water being colorless. He comments that because it is clear, we can inspect it before drinking to see if there are any impurities.

62
FULLY STOCKED

*M*r. Azar was tight on time. He had flown out to Memphis, Tennessee, on a business trip and now it was too close to Shabbos to fly back to New York. He was far away from home with no plans for meals. He rushed into the nearest hotel and asked for a room.

"We're pretty empty today," the clerk said. "You can have any room you wish."

"I'm in quite a rush," Mr. Azar replied. "I'll take anything, as long as I can settle in quickly."

It was a large hotel. The clerk gave him the keys to room 358. He opened the closet to put away his clothing and could not believe what he saw. It was fully stocked with Shabbos food! There was challah, wine, and packaged meat. He even found pickles and olives; clearly this was all left by a Jew.

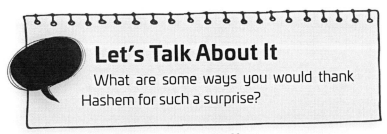

Let's Talk About It

What are some ways you would thank Hashem for such a surprise?

See page 248 for possible answers.

He thanked Hashem and enjoyed the pleasant surprise.

Upon his return home, he heard that a man from his community had been in Memphis shortly before him. He had stayed in the very same hotel as Mr. Azar. He had planned to spend Shabbos there but changed his mind at the last minute. In his haste, he left the food behind. Mr. Azar marveled at the beautiful *hashgachah pratis* and thanked Hashem for allowing him to spend Shabbos in comfort.

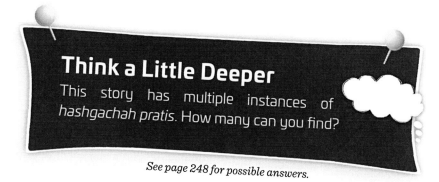

Think a Little Deeper

This story has multiple instances of hashgachah pratis. How many can you find?

See page 248 for possible answers.

It Happened to Me!

Can you think of a time you found that a solution to your problem was there from before? Share YOUR *hashgachah pratis* story.

63
OFFER OF A LIFETIME

There was once a king who loved his subjects dearly. He was always looking for opportunities to give them gifts and do them favors.

One day, the king invited a peasant to meet with him in the royal palace. The peasant arrived in his simple clothing, wondering what the meeting would be about.

The king welcomed the man with a kind smile. "Today I am going to make you the offer of a lifetime," he said. "I want to give you a prominent position in my palace with very important tasks."

The peasant stared at the king, eyes wide and mouth agape.

But the king wasn't done yet. "From now on, you are going to live with royalty. You will wear a royal uniform and eat sumptuous meals. I will assign you many special jobs, and for every job you will earn one million gold coins."

By now, the peasant could barely contain himself.

"One million gold coins?!"

"Yes. There will be times you find yourself thoroughly enjoying a particular job, but you will still get paid for it. Some jobs are easy and some are difficult. The harder the mission, the more I will pay you. You can even earn 100 million gold coins in a single moment."

The king continued with his fantastic offer. "I will also give you a paid vacation one day a week. For that day, you can buy the most expensive meats and delicacies and I will pay for all of it. In fact, if you rest properly on that day, I will reward you so greatly you will never be able to count it up."

The peasant's head was spinning with images of this magical lifestyle. The king kept talking, describing the unlimited opportunity of the offer.

"If you ever have a request," the king said, "I want you to feel perfectly comfortable asking me. I will be available for you at all hours of the day, every day of the year. I will reward you greatly just for submitting your request, and every time you ask again, I will double and triple the reward."

Let's Talk About It

This story is a *mashal*. Let's figure out the *nimshal*. Who is the king? Who is the peasant? What are the "jobs" and what is the "reward"? What is the weekly "paid vacation day"?

See page 248 for possible answers.

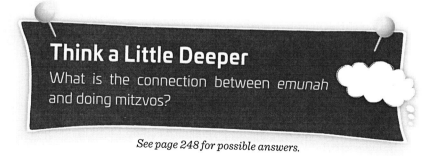

Think a Little Deeper

What is the connection between *emunah* and doing mitzvos?

See page 248 for possible answers.

64
DETOUR BY DESIGN

ebbetzin Chaya Mushka Schneerson used to take a daily walk in the park. Her driver, Mr. Chesed Halberstam, would take her there. They always followed the same route.

One day, Mr. Halberstam noticed that the road they usually used was being repaired. It was entirely blocked off and he had to take a different street instead. As they drove along, they heard the sound of someone crying. The Rebbetzin asked her driver if they could stop and check if everything was okay. They followed the sound until they met up with a woman crying on the sidewalk. She was surrounded by furniture and household items. Workers were in the process of loading her belongings onto a nearby truck.

The Rebbetzin approached the distressed woman. "Can we help you?" she asked.

"I have not been able to pay rent for several months,

and now I'm being evicted," she sobbed. A city marshal was standing a few feet away, overseeing the eviction.

The Rebbetzin asked Mr. Halberstam to find out from the marshal how much money the woman owed, and if he would accept a personal check.

"The balance is $6,700. If I can confirm with the bank that the transaction will go through, I can accept a personal check," the marshal replied.

On the spot, the Rebbetzin took out her checkbook and wrote out the full amount. The marshal contacted the bank and was told that the money was cleared for transfer.

"Return all items to this woman's apartment immediately," the marshal ordered his workers.

Once the Rebbetzin saw that the woman would be taken care of, she urged Mr. Halberstam, "Let's drive away quickly, before she realizes what happened."

Let's Talk About It

The woman never found out who paid up her balance. How often does Hashem arrange things for us, without us ever finding out? Let's thank Hashem for all His hidden *chasadim*.

When they finally arrived at the park, Rebbetzin Chaya Mushka explained to Mr. Halberstam why she had helped out a total stranger.

"Once, when I was very young, my father took me for a walk. We talked about *hashgachah pratis*, how every step we take is literally orchestrated by Hashem. He said to me, 'When something causes us to deviate from our normal routine, it has been designed by Hashem for a reason and we have to recognize that.'"

"Today," the Rebbetzin continued, "when I saw us taking a detour, I remembered my father's words. I started looking out for a possible reason why Hashem might have led us through this particular route. When I heard the woman's cries I thought that maybe that was the special reason, so I helped her."

Think a Little Deeper

There is no such thing as coincidence. Can you think of some reasons why Hashem would cause us to be delayed with a detour or get stuck in traffic?

See page 248 for possible answers.

65
A PROTECTIVE SHIELD

Boris was a Jewish boy who was raised in Russia. His mother was religious, but because of the laws against teaching Torah, he grew up not knowing much about his Jewishness.

Boris married Miriam, a Jewish girl from a similar background. Her mother was also religious and was always praying, but Miriam herself was raised secular.

After a few years, Boris moved to America with his wife and mother-in-law. Here they lived with greater freedom and life was good. Sadly, Miriam's mother got sick and passed away.

One month later, Miriam herself became ill. She was diagnosed with a terrible disease and the doctors said she had only a few weeks left to live. Boris was beside himself. *What's going on here?* he thought. *First my mother-in-law passes away, and now my wife gets sick?*

Then he realized something. Maybe his mother-in-law's prayers had been helping their family all these years. Now that she was gone and no one was praying for them, that protection wasn't there anymore.

Let's Talk About It
What are some things Boris can do to try to improve the situation?

See page 249 for possible answers.

Boris did not know the first thing about praying, but he knew he had to start. He bravely walked into a shul and talked to Hashem in his own words. Then he turned to one of the men there.

"Can you teach me how to pray?" he asked.

This was the first step in Boris' journey toward becoming fully religious. Two months after he started praying, he got a call from a prestigious hospital.

"We heard about your wife's condition," a doctor said. "We would like to offer you an experimental treatment. It has helped people in similar situations live an additional eighteen months."

With no better options, Boris and Miriam agreed. *Baruch Hashem,* the treatment was successful and Miriam lived another nine healthy years.

Think a Little Deeper
Can you think of a time you saw how your prayers made a difference?

Great People, Great *Emunah*

Sometimes we pray for something and we don't get the answer we wanted.

Why does this happen? Where do those *tefillos* go?

When the Steipler Gaon was ill, thousands of Jews prayed for his recovery. In the end, the tzaddik passed away. Somebody remarked to his son, Harav Chaim Kanievsky, that all the prayers that had been recited for his father were useless. Rav Chaim replied, "I know for a fact that those prayers nullified a decree that would have affected a large number of people."

No *tefillah* ever goes to waste.

66
FIRST LINE OF DEFENSE

*I*t covers the entire body. It keeps the good things in and the bad things out. It serves as the first line of defense against disease. What is the name of this special covering? Skin!

What is skin and how does it work?

The skin is the largest organ. It has many different jobs. Most obviously, it protects us from germs and dirt in the outside environment. The skin's thickness varies to accommodate specific body parts. Your eyelids, for example, have thinner skin than the soles of your feet.

The skin has thousands of sensors that feel what we touch. These sensors tell the brain if something is hot, cold, rough, smooth, or painful. Our hands, feet, and lips have extra sensors, making them especially sensitive.

Let's Talk About It

Think of three things you felt with your skin today. How would your life be different without the sense of touch?

See page 249 for possible answers.

Temperature control is another one of the skin's jobs. It absorbs sunlight for heat and regulates our body temperature. When the body gets hot, the skin sweats to cool off. It can also cause nearby blood vessels to widen and cool off even more. When the body is cold, the skin narrows blood vessels in order to warm up.

Think a Little Deeper

How can learning about our wonderful skin help build our emunah?

See page 249 for possible answers.

Great People, Great *Emunah*

It was during the winter, and Rabbi Menachem Mendel of Riminov wanted to travel somewhere. He could not afford to pay for the wagon, so he offered to assist the driver by tending to the horses whenever the driver needed to stop and rest.

They began their journey, and soon it was time to make a stop. The driver went into a roadside inn while Rabbi Menachem Mendel stayed outside with the horses, shivering in the bitter cold. He realized that if he didn't move around, he would freeze. He moved his arms and legs and began jumping.

The great Rabbi thought to himself, *If I am already jumping, why not turn it into a joyful dance? I will use this opportunity to sing and praise Hashem.*

Rabbi Menachem Mendel did exactly that. In middle of his holy dance, a man stepped outside the inn.

"What are you doing?!" he asked the Rabbi.

"I am thanking Hashem," the Rabbi replied. "There are many people who are too sick to move around. Yet I can be active! There are people who are too ill to notice when they are hungry. Yet I am well enough to feel hunger pains. There is so much for me to be grateful for."

The man was very moved. He paid some stable boys to watch the horses and invited Rabbi Menachem Mendel in for a hot meal.

67
STUCK IN A TRUCK

*E*phraim hummed a tune as he expertly steered his truck along the highway. He was transporting a load of chickens from Pennsylvania to New York.

About midway through the journey, Ephraim found himself caught in a heavy blizzard. Visibility was very poor. He turned onto a side street and carefully continued driving. As he focused on the road ahead, he noticed a car stranded in a ditch.

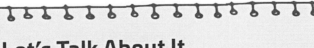

Let's Talk About It

It's freezing cold. Ephraim can drive right past the car and no one would ever know. What would you do in this situation? What would Hashem want you to do?

See page 249 for possible answers.

Ephraim stopped his truck and got out to investigate. The icy winds made it difficult to breathe. He slowly approached the car and tapped on the driver's window.

"Are you okay?" he called out.

"Not really," the man said. "We skidded on some ice and swerved into this ditch. Now we're stuck." Ephraim noticed that the man's wife seemed anxious. There were three small children in the back.

"You can't stay here all night," Ephraim protested. "Come join me in my truck. I'll take you to a place where you can get some sleep."

The family was so thankful. They huddled together as Ephraim drove slowly, looking out for a motel. A few miles later, they found one and parked. They all went in and approached the clerk at the front desk.

"I'm really sorry," the clerk said. "We are totally booked. You can try the next motel, 20 miles up the road."

Ephraim understood that in such weather, the other place would be full as well. "Please," he said, "this family just survived an accident and they have nowhere to stay. They have three young children. Perhaps you can find them somewhere to rest?"

"Well," the clerk replied, "for a small fee, they can sleep here in the lobby."

Ephraim reached into his pocket and paid for the family's stay. They were very appreciative.

"Thank you," the father said emotionally. "You saved our lives. I will never forget this. You showed my whole family just how kind a person can be."

By now Ephraim was many hours late. He got right back into his truck and drove to New York.

Twenty years passed. Ephraim was once again driving from Pennsylvania to New York. By now, he had a newer, updated truck. Suddenly, the engine started sputtering and he was forced to pull over. He realized that he was out of gas.

That's weird, Ephraim said to himself. *The gauge shows a quarter of a tank. I guess it's broken.*

Ephraim sat in his truck, wondering how he could get to the next service station and bring back a container of gas. As he tried to think of a plan, a car pulled up behind him.

"Hey, you need help?" the driver called out.

"Well, yes," Ephraim replied. He explained his predicament.

"I'm happy to help out," the man said, smiling. "Come join me in my car."

He happily helped Ephraim get gas and then brought him back to his truck. Ephraim took out some money and offered to pay the fellow for his time.

"Oh, I can't take money for that," he said. "I try to help people, especially those on the side of the road. You know, I was once helped by a Jewish man with a truckload of chickens. He rescued me and my family in middle of a blizzard and drove us to a motel. He even paid for it."

Ephraim's eyes opened wide. "I'm that man!" he exclaimed. "I never forgot that cold winter night. I can't believe I got to meet you again."

Think a Little Deeper
Who can arrange such an unlikely reunion? It can only be Hashem!

It Happened to Me!
Have you ever experienced *middah k'neged middah*? Share YOUR *hashgachah pratis* story!

68
AT YOUR FINGERTIPS

ali bounced into her house with a huge smile. Today her mother would be arriving home from the hospital with her brand-new baby sister! The older children scurried around to clean up in preparation for the exciting moment.

Mali leaned against the window, waiting for the family car.

"They're here!" she called.

Everyone rushed to the door to greet their mother and the baby.

"Wow, she's beautiful," Mali breathed. "So tiny, and so perfect."

"Yes, *baruch Hashem*. A few years ago, you were about this size too." Her mother smiled. "Soon our baby will grow into a beautiful, mature young lady just like her big sister." She patted Mali's head.

The next morning Mali woke up early, excited about her new sister. She found her mother already in the kitchen, washing the baby's tiny hands. The baby looked calm and re-laxed. Mali reached out with a fresh towel to dry the baby's fingers.

"One, two, three..." She counted her sister's little fingers one by one. Mali's mother laughed.

"I did the same thing in the hospital," she said. "As soon as my children are born, I count their fingers and toes and marvel at how perfect they are, *baruch Hashem*. Did you know, Mali, that every finger has a special job?"

Mali sat down beside her mother on the couch.

"The thumb can move in many directions, and helps the other fingers grasp things. The index finger is the best at fine movements, which is why you use it to direct your pencil when you write or draw."

Mali leaned closer as her mother continued, "The biggest and stron-gest finger is right in middle, and is supported by its neighbor, the ring finger. And of course, the little pinky has the special advantage of fitting into small spaces."

Mali wriggled her fingers and leaned closer to the new baby. The ba-by's fists were clenched tight, ten priceless blessings.

Let's Talk About It

Can you name five tasks that would be impossible without your fingers?

See page 249 for possible answers.

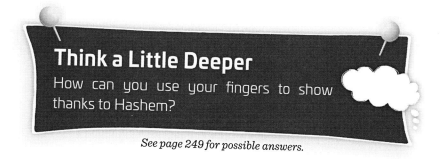

Think a Little Deeper

How can you use your fingers to show thanks to Hashem?

See page 249 for possible answers.

69
LONG-TERM BENEFIT

Mrs. Natalie Cohen was a very special woman. Although she had a serious illness, she worked on herself to stay upbeat and positive. Mrs. Cohen spoke of her challenges to other women and inspired them to live their lives with awareness of Hashem's goodness, even in times of difficulty.

Mrs. Cohen was often in the hospital for treatment. One day, a woman approached her and asked if she was Jewish.

"I am," she answered proudly. "Are you Jewish too?"

"Yes, but I am not observant," the woman said. Her tone turned bitter. "I don't understand how G-d can make young people sick."

With great patience and gentleness, Mrs. Cohen asked the other woman if she vaccinated her children.

"Of course I do!" she replied.

"But why would you allow a doctor to give painful

injections to your small children?"

The woman laughed, explaining that injections protected the child from harmful diseases in the future. The small, passing pain was worth the great benefit it provided.

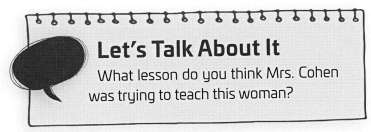

Let's Talk About It

What lesson do you think Mrs. Cohen was trying to teach this woman?

See page 249 for possible answers.

"My friend," Mrs. Cohen said, "right now, my loving Father is vaccinating me. It hurts, but it's for my long-term benefit."

Mrs. Natalie Cohen was able to see a higher purpose to what happens in this world. She reframed her physical pain and saw it as the best possible thing for her neshamah. She fully believed that Hashem was treating her with love and that everything He sent her way was for her best interest.

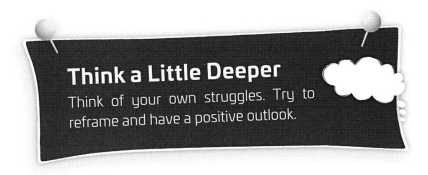

Think a Little Deeper

Think of your own struggles. Try to reframe and have a positive outlook.

Great People, Great *Emunah*

It was Seder night in the home of the holy Chasam Sofer. His son, the Ksav Sofer, was still a child. He asked his father an excellent question, but his father did not respond.

All night, the young Ksav Sofer wondered about his question.

The next morning, the Chasam Sofer lovingly called over his son and delivered a beautiful, clear answer to the question.

"Father, did you already have this response last night?" asked the little boy.

"I did, my child."

"But Father, you saw how disturbed I was, how badly I wanted clarity," the Ksav Sofer said. "If you had the answer then, why didn't you share it with me right away?"

"My dear child, I wanted to teach you a valuable lesson. In life, we often need to wait a while to find out why certain things happen. Some things we will only understand in the Next World. It is important to train ourselves to have *emunah* and believe that there *are* answers, there are reasons, even though we don't always know what they are."

70
INVESTMENT TO BANK ON

ax Schwartz smoothed out his best business suit. He was in Detroit for an important meeting at a bank. If all went well, he would walk out with a large sum of money to invest in his business.

The meeting was scheduled for 4:30 p.m. With an hour to spare, Max looked around the area for a shul where he could pray Minchah. He found one nearby that had a sign saying that Minchah was scheduled for 4 o' clock.

Perfect, he thought. *I will pray here, and then head over to the bank for the meeting.*

Precisely at four, he entered the shul. There were only two other people there. He sat down to wait for the *minyan* to fill up. People trickled in slowly as the minutes ticked by.

It wasn't until 4:25 that the tenth man walked in. By now Max really had to leave. He tapped the *chazzan* on the shoulder and said, "I'm only going to stay for the silent *Shemoneh Esrei*. I need to leave right after that."

The *chazzan* looked at him pleadingly. "Please," he said, "I need to say *Kaddish*. Would you please stay for the entire *tefillah*?"

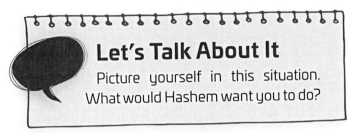

Let's Talk About It
Picture yourself in this situation.
What would Hashem want you to do?

See page 249 for possible answers.

Max was torn. The biggest meeting of his life was waiting for him. He closed his eyes, and with great self-sacrifice said to the man, "Okay, I'll stay."

As soon as Minchah was over, he dashed over to the bank. He was 15 minutes late. Still panting from the run, he approached the secretary and introduced himself.

"You're late," she said. "But don't worry. The executive is not here yet."

Max took a moment to catch his breath. He was grateful he wasn't the only one that was delayed. After a brief wait, the secretary called his name. She directed him toward the room where the meeting would take place.

When he opened the door, Max found himself face to face with the *chazzan* who had just asked him to stay for *Kaddish*! The executive shook his hand warmly and said, "It's nice to see you again. Thank you for staying for me."

Max opened and closed his mouth, speechless.

"You risked missing this meeting to help me out," the banker continued. "Now I am going to do my best to help you."

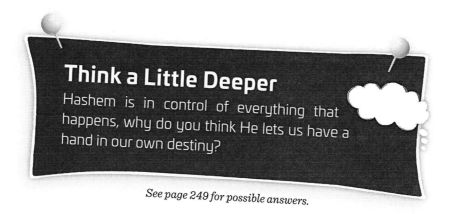

Think a Little Deeper

Hashem is in control of everything that happens, why do you think He lets us have a hand in our own destiny?

See page 249 for possible answers.

71
THE
INCREDIBLE FORK

Pinchas's muscles felt sore, but his face was shining. Hiking was his favorite camp activity. Today he was trekking through a hilly forest with his bunk and their counselor, Tzvi.

"Ten more minutes and then we stop for a picnic lunch!" shouted Tzvi. "We're almost there, boys. We can do this! When we get to a clearing we'll take a break and eat."

The group scrambled over the remaining distance and dumped their backpacks down on the rocky surface, tired and proud.

"It feels so good to finally be here," Benny smiled. "Look how high we are."

"Yes," agreed Pinchas. "And the fresh smell of trees makes me want to live outdoors forever!"

"What about the insects and animals we saw before? Are you sure you want to live with them?" asked Benny.

Pinchas laughed. "Everything is so beautiful and peaceful here. It's amazing. The bugs and birds live here and nobody has to come feed them. The squirrels, deer, and even the trees..."

Their counselor passed around sandwiches and the boys settled down.

"Tzvi, tell us a story," someone called out.

"Tell us a story! Tell us a story!" echoed the rest of the group.

"I have a story for you, boys," Tzvi grinned. "But I'm not going to tell you whether it's true or not until the end."

He held up a plastic fork from his lunch. "Listen to the fascinating history of this fork," he began.

"One day, a toy factory received a shipment of white sheets of plastic. Workers unloaded the plastic into a special warehouse for storage. Special engineers planned designs for new toys, and the white plastic boards would be turned into different shapes and colors."

The boys munched their sandwiches while their counselor continued. "That night, after all the workers went home, there was an explosion in the warehouse. The building burst into flames. Inside, huge metal shelves and plastic sheets crashed together. The intense heat caused the metal to mold the molten white plastic into a perfectly symmetrical design."

Tzvi waved the fork dramatically in the air. "And that, my friends, is how this fork was formed."

Benny looked skeptical.

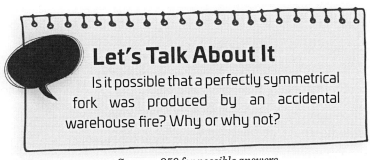

Let's Talk About It

Is it possible that a perfectly symmetrical fork was produced by an accidental warehouse fire? Why or why not?

See page 250 for possible answers.

See page 250 for possible answers.

Pinchas jumped up and burst out, "How is that possible? This fork is too perfect! It must have been designed and produced in a huge factory with exact measurements. How can such a perfect fork come about by *accident*?!"

"Ah," Tzvi smiled. "So you don't believe my story. Good thinking, Pinchas. Who else feels that way?"

Hands shot up all around.

"Boys, you are absolutely right. When we look at the details of this plastic fork, we realize it must have been created with a plan and a purpose."

Benny called out, "We were just talking about this. The forest is full of perfection everywhere you look. The trees grow, they produce leaves, the animals have food and shelter — you can see Hashem's design all over nature."

"You boys are right on track." Their counselor beamed. "We know Hashem created the world and everything in it. When we look closely at His creations, like the beauty of this forest, we realize more and more that Hashem designed the world with brilliance and with purpose. None of this is a mistake. None of this happened by accident."

72
IT COULD HAVE BEEN ME

*E*zra's grandfather lived in California. He was having kidney failure and his family decided that it would be best for him to move to New York for treatment. They asked Ezra to help his grandfather gather his belongings and transport them to New York.

Ezra loved his grandfather and was happy to help out. His brother booked him an early morning flight so there would be enough time to pack everything up and return the next day.

The day before the flight, he got a call from his brother.

"I was thinking about your trip," he said. "It might be a better idea if you flew tonight so that you can rest up when you arrive. This way you'll have more energy tomorrow for all the packing."

Ezra got a new ticket and landed safely in California. He went straight to his grandfather's home and slept a peaceful night's sleep.

The next morning was a day that will forever be remembered in history. United flight 175 from Boston was hijacked and crashed into the South Tower of the World Trade Center. *This was the flight Ezra was originally booked for!*

Ezra's parents were not aware of the last-minute ticket change. As soon as they heard the news of the hijacking they went into a state of panic. When Ezra called, they were shocked to hear his voice.

To this day, Ezra becomes emotional every time he repeats the story of this amazing miracle. A last-minute ticket change saved his life.

Let's Talk About It
What can we learn from this story?

See page 250 for possible answers.

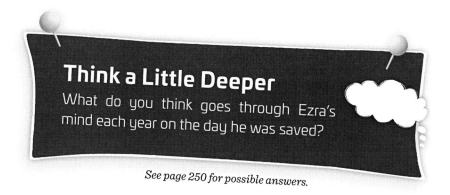

Think a Little Deeper
What do you think goes through Ezra's mind each year on the day he was saved?

See page 250 for possible answers.

73

HOW CAN I EVER REPAY YOU?

Mark was in a serious car accident. He lay in his hospital bed waiting for the doctor's report. The doctor entered the room and in a grave tone he said, "You are very lucky to be alive. We will continue to treat you and do the best we can. However, your left eye is no longer able to see."

Mark was devastated. As soon as he was discharged, he scheduled an appointment with a top specialist. The specialist examined Mark and administered several tests. But when the results came in, the doctor said there was nothing he could do.

Mark traveled from doctor to doctor, hoping to find a cure to reverse the blindness.

One day, a medical facility in California contacted Mark. They said they were working on a new experimental procedure for certain cases of damaged vision. They had developed a surgery that could potentially restore eyesight. Mark booked a ticket immediately and the very next day he met the surgeon in California.

For a full week, he underwent a series of scans and preparations. When the day of the procedure arrived, he was filled with nervous excitement. Would it be successful?

"The surgery is complex and it will take some time for you to recover," warned the doctor. "Your eyes must remain covered for a few hours and only then will we know if your eyesight has returned."

After the surgery, Mark's eyes were protected with layers of bandages. When the anesthesia wore off, the doctor arrived. Slowly, he removed the bandages...

"I can see!" cried Mark. "Thank you, Doctor! I can finally see!" Mark remained grateful to this doctor for the rest of his life. *I wish there was some way I could repay him,* he thought.

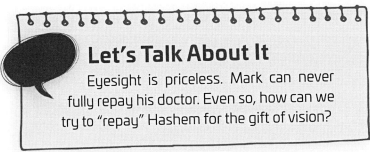

Let's Talk About It

Eyesight is priceless. Mark can never fully repay his doctor. Even so, how can we try to "repay" Hashem for the gift of vision?

See page 250 for possible answers.

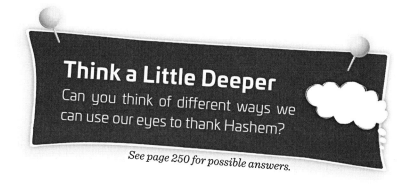

Think a Little Deeper

Can you think of different ways we can use our eyes to thank Hashem?

See page 250 for possible answers.

74
A NEW LEASE ON LIFE

*R*av Eliyahu Lopian set out on a mission for the yeshivah of Kelm, Lithuania. The yeshivah was deeply in debt and the Rav planned to raise money from fellow Jews in the surrounding areas. He invested a great deal of time and effort into his fundraising mission. After many long weeks, he finally succeeded and prepared to return back home.

On his way to the train station, Rav Eliyahu asked somebody for directions. The man offered to personally escort the Rav there. They passed through a dark, deserted alleyway.

"Are you sure this is the right way to the train station?" Rav Eliyahu asked his escort.

"Don't worry," the man said. "We'll be there soon." Suddenly, he whipped out a gun and stole all the money the Rav was carrying. The yeshivah funds that Rav Eliyahu had worked so hard to collect were gone in an instant.

Rav Eliyahu returned to his inn, penniless. He debated whether he should start fundraising all over again or just return to Kelm empty-handed.

He decided to try collecting again. He traveled far away to countries he had never been to before. For the first time in his life, he went to England. Hashem blessed his efforts with success and soon he obtained the full sum the yeshivah needed. Meanwhile, the Jewish community in England became very connected to the Rav and asked him to remain and fill a Rabbinical position. Rav Eliyahu accepted and brought his family over to join him in London. He became the Rosh Yeshivah of Yeshivah Etz Chaim in the East End of London.

A few years later, the Nazis swept through Lithuania. Rav Eliyahu Lopian was the only survivor of his town. He spent the rest of his life disseminating Torah and lived into his 90s.

Let's Talk About It

Rav Eliyahu Lopian did not give up. How does this demonstrate his *emunah*?

See page 250 for possible answers.

Think a Little Deeper

How did Rav Eliyahu's *emunah* save his life?

See page 250 for possible answers.

Great People, Great *Emunah*

The Chafetz Chaim once asked someone how he was doing.

"Could be better," the person replied with a groan.

"You are making a mistake," the Chafetz Chaim said. "If things were different, they would not be better. Hashem knows precisely what is best for every person."

75

I JUST WANT TO HEAR YOUR VOICE

Michael was a beautiful little boy who was the pride and joy of his parents. He was their only child, and they went to great lengths to provide him with the best childhood possible.

Sadly, when Michael grew older, he fell in with the wrong crowd. He veered off the path of Yiddishkeit and engaged in all sorts of destructive behavior. His parents were devastated.

One night, Michael threw a grand party for his friends in his parents' house. The crowd became drunk, destroying the furniture, walls, and floors. By the end of the party, the unruly group had caused thousands of dollars of damage to the house.

Michael was so ashamed. He couldn't face his parents, so he left home and went to live with one of his friends.

Michael's parents were now more pained than before. Although he was a wayward son, they still wanted to stay close with him. They decided to seek professional help.

They approached a well-known expert who knew how to guide children back to the right path. They told him where Michael lived and he reached out to the troubled young man. Soon, the professional reported back to Michael's father that his son was making good progress.

Michael's father was overjoyed. He tried calling his son, but there was no answer. He knocked on his door and was able to see his son through the window, but still, Michael wouldn't open the door.

In tears, the father went back to the professional.

"What should I do?" he cried. "How can I possibly get my son to talk to me again?"

The man sensed the father's raw pain and asked Michael, "You are growing so nicely. Why don't you speak to your father?"

Michael looked down in shame and said, "I owe him tens of thousands of dollars. I have no way of paying him back. How can I possibly talk to him? What will I say when he asks me for the money?"

The man placed his arm around the broken young man. "Your father doesn't care about money right now. He wants you. He wants to hear your voice, to see your face. That is worth more to him than any money in the world."

Let's Talk About It

Even if we have done wrong, we must remember that Hashem is our loving Father. He just wants us to do *teshuvah* and come close to Him.

Think a Little Deeper

How does having *emunah* help a person do *teshuvah*?

See page 250 for possible answers.

76
THE REAL DEAL

aron ran a busy real estate business. All day, he worked on contracts and earned enough money to support his family comfortably.

One day, a great opportunity came up. Aaron became very involved in meetings and conferences, spending hours and hours in his office.

After several weeks, all the details fell into place and the deal was signed. This was a huge accomplishment for the company and Aaron was very satisfied. He met his friend Chaim and shared the good news.

"Baruch Hashem," Chaim said as he shook Aaron's hand. "I'm so glad Hashem made this deal work for you."

Aaron was annoyed. He had spent many late nights at the office working on this contract. "What does

Hashem have to do with this?" he grumbled. "I am in charge of my business, and I made a good decision!"

Let's Talk About It
What is Aaron's mistake?

See page 251 for possible answers.

Chaim sat down with his friend. "You understand that Hashem makes the sun shine. You believe Hashem makes your heart beat, correct?"

Aaron nodded.

Chaim continued, "Today Hashem blessed you with a successful deal and suddenly you're taking the credit. Hashem is no less involved in your money than He is in nature! The same Creator Who makes your heart beat is the One Who decided your business should go well."

Aaron grew thoughtful. Could it be that he was just a player in Hashem's big plan?

"You're right," he admitted to his friend. "This deal could just as easily have gone to my competitors. Instead, Hashem sent it to me. *Baruch Hashem!*"

Think a Little Deeper
Can you describe one thing that you accomplished recently? Can you find Hashem in the picture?

77

MINI-MIRACLE

One Monday morning, Rabbi Fried woke up with laryngitis. He felt fine, except he could barely speak. He planned to spend the day learning quietly and sipping tea.

As Rabbi Fried prepared a hot drink, his phone rang. It was the principal of a nearby school, asking him to come fill in as a substitute teacher.

"I'm sorry, I'm not available to teach today," Rabbi Fried whispered hoarsely into the phone. "My voice is gone."

The principal was desperate. "Please," he pleaded. "It's a large class and if you don't come, it will be really chaotic. Even if you can just supervise, or maybe teach something in a low voice, you would really save the day."

Rabbi Fried reluctantly agreed.

He arrived at the school a few minutes early and went to the cafeteria to fix himself a tea. Hopefully, this would help out his voice. To his dismay, there wasn't a tea bag in sight. The school was out of tea. Now he was really stuck.

With no other choice, Rabbi Fried went to class and tried to teach. He was supposed to substitute for about four hours. Thirty minutes into the class, a boy walked in and excused himself for being late.

"I was at a *bris* this morning," he said. Then he walked up to Rabbi Fried and said, "I really wanted to bring the rebbi a plate of food from the *bris milah*. But by the time I remembered, everything was cleared away."

The boy stuck his hand into his pocket and placed a few tea bags on the rebbi's desk. "I felt bad to come empty-handed so I brought you a few packets of tea. This is all that was left."

Rabbi Fried stared at the boy in wonder. "Wow, this is *min haShamayim!* This is exactly what I needed. Thank you!"

Let's Talk About It

How does Hashem's *hashgachah pratis* show His love for us?

See page 251 for possible answers.

Think a Little Deeper

Hashem is just as involved in the little details as He is with the big things. Hashem often performs mini-miracles in our daily lives, and it is a mitzvah to tell them to others and spread the *kiddush Hashem*.

It Happened to Me!

Did you experience a mini-miracle recently? Make a *kiddush Hashem* and share YOUR story.

Hashem cares about me so much!

78
GREAT IDEA!

*T*he human mind is the most powerful and least understood gift we have. Scientists admit that after intense research and study, they still know very little about the human brain.

This is what we do know. The brain is the grand processing center for everything we experience. More than 80 billion neurons work together to interpret what we see, hear, taste, touch, and smell. The brain sorts this information, discards unimportant details, and stores others in a complex system called memory. The mind is where all thinking, feeling, and planning takes place.

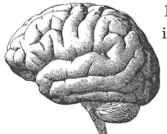

No plant or animal has the same capacity as a human being, because no other creation needs such a powerhouse processing system in order to fulfill its G-dly mission.

It is up to each person to choose how to use their powerful mind, and it is up to each person to thank Hashem for gifting it to them.

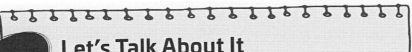

Let's Talk About It

See how many ways you can complete this sentence:
"Thank You, Hashem, for my brain because..."

See page 251 for possible answers.

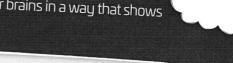

Think a Little Deeper

How can we use our brains in a way that shows thanks to Hashem?

See page 251 for possible answers.

Great People, Great *Emunah*

Rabbi Gershon Liebman of France is credited with leading 80,000 Jews in becoming *baalei teshuvah*. His students compiled his lectures into a book and presented him with a copy. A group of students looked on as Rabbi Liebman read through some of the pages for the first time.

"Wow," he exclaimed, "these are beautiful Torah insights!"

The students were taken aback. They knew their Rabbi to be very humble. They could not understand the uncharacteristic boasting. They asked him why he praised his own work so highly.

Rabbi Liebman smiled and responded, "Just because Hashem allowed these novel Torah thoughts to pass through my brain, does that mean I did anything?"

The next time you think of a great idea, pause and thank Hashem for your incredible brain.

79
IRREPLACEABLE LOYALTY

abbi Schreiber spent his day studying in yeshivah. His wife was a teacher. The Schreibers employed a loyal babysitter named Batya, who cared for the children every day until their parents came home.

Batya had no children of her own. She scheduled an appointment with a special doctor to see what could be done. This was an important appointment and she had to wait three months for it.

At last, the day arrived. Batya was on the way to the doctor's office when suddenly she stopped in her tracks.

"I forgot to tell the Schreibers that I would not be available to babysit today!" she realized. "The Rav is in yeshivah and his wife has a classroom of students waiting for her. If I don't show up to watch the children, the Rav will stay home and lose a day of Torah learning."

Batya was not sure what to do. The doctor was booked and

it was difficult to get an appointment with him. But it was too late to find a replacement to babysit for the Schreibers.

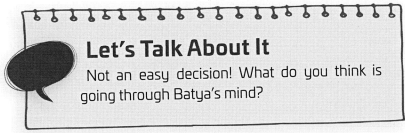

Let's Talk About It

Not an easy decision! What do you think is going through Batya's mind?

See page 251 for possible answers.

"I will babysit the children as usual," Batya decided. "I can reschedule this appointment and wait another three months to see the doctor." She figured that next time she would make arrangements for a replacement in advance.

Batya turned around and headed toward the Schreiber home. She babysat the children with her usual smile and warmth, and Rabbi and Mrs. Schreiber were able to keep to their regular schedule.

Batya did not end up needing to see the specialist. Instead, Hashem made a miracle for her and that year, she gave birth to a beautiful, healthy baby boy. He grew up to be an outstanding *talmid chacham* who brought Batya and her husband tremendous *nachas*.

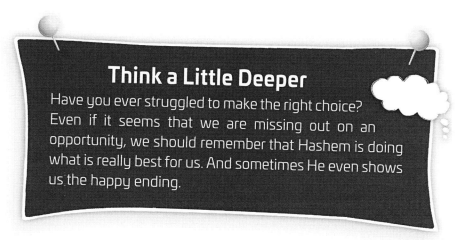

Think a Little Deeper

Have you ever struggled to make the right choice? Even if it seems that we are missing out on an opportunity, we should remember that Hashem is doing what is really best for us. And sometimes He even shows us the happy ending.

Let's Reframe With *Emunah* Glasses

Picture this scenario:

The Purim carnival is in full swing. It is almost your turn at the cotton candy booth. Suddenly you notice a little girl crying. She seems lost and confused.

If you go over to offer help, you might lose your place in line.

But the child needs help, and you want to help her find a responsible adult.

Think: How would Hashem want me to act? How can I reframe and see things with "*emunah* glasses"?

80
CAR
COLORS

The Teichmans had outgrown their car. It would have been nice to upgrade to a larger one, but they couldn't afford it.

Mr. Teichman asked around and found out about a car dealer who worked with families on tight budgets. Although he was a bit uncomfortable asking for help, he called the dealer and told him how much he could afford.

"Don't worry," the kind man said. "I'll check what's available and I'll get back to you."

A few days later, the dealer contacted the Teichmans and said he had found a suitable car for a reasonable price. "If you let me know what color you like, I can get it for you by the end of the week," he said.

Mr. Teichman was so appreciative. He asked his wife if she had a color preference, and her response was immediate. "I saw that car in green the other day," she said. "It looked really nice. Please ask him for a green one."

Mr. Teichman called the dealer right away and told him his wife's reply.

The very next day, Mrs. Teichman saw the same car in silver and she liked it much better than the green. She asked her husband, "Can you ask the dealer to arrange for a silver one?"

"I'm afraid it's too late," he replied. "The guy called today to say the green one is ready. It wouldn't be right to switch. After all, he's doing us a favor."

Mrs. Teichman was disappointed. She really wanted the silver version. All day, it was on her mind.

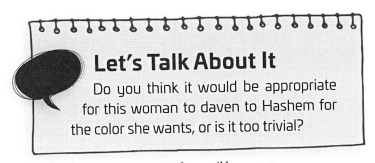

Let's Talk About It

Do you think it would be appropriate for this woman to daven to Hashem for the color she wants, or is it too trivial?

See page 251 for possible answers.

That night, car colors were still on her mind. "Hashem," she said, "I know I shouldn't care so much about these things. Please help me grow to a level where I care about more important matters than the color of my car."

This helped her relax about the whole thing. She still wished for the silver model, but she felt more at peace with the green.

The next morning, the man from the dealership contacted the Teichmans. "Last night there was a break-in and one car was stolen. It was yours. I'm sorry about the delay but I need to order a new one and it will take another few days."

"No problem at all," Mr. Teichman said. "Would it be possible for you to get us a silver one?"

"Sure," the man said. "I'll let you know when it arrives."

Sure enough, a very pleased Mrs. Teichman was soon driving her silver car.

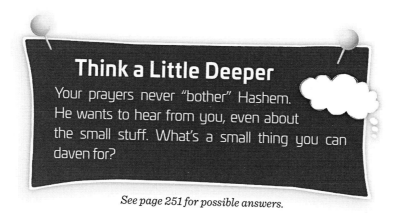

Think a Little Deeper

Your prayers never "bother" Hashem. He wants to hear from you, even about the small stuff. What's a small thing you can daven for?

See page 251 for possible answers.

81
PUMPED!

*I*t's automatic, it runs on schedule, and it works non-stop. It's as small as your fist, yet it's responsible for delivering oxygen to your entire body. Do you know of a more efficient pump than your heart?

Your heart is a powerhouse.

Hashem created the heart to function as a double pump. The right side pumps blood to the lungs for oxygen. The left side pumps oxygenated blood from the lungs to the body. Your body parts need oxygen in order to survive, so your heart never rests.

Your busy heart beats 100,000 times per day, pumping five to six quarts of blood per minute. One of the amazing features of your heart is the way it keeps up with your varying activities. When you run around a lot, you need more oxygen-filled blood.

This is why your heart beats faster when you exercise; it is pumping at a faster rate.

You may also feel your heart rate increase when you feel afraid. This is your body preparing to run or protect itself if necessary.

Imagine if you had to be on top of your heart, constantly reminding it to do its many jobs. You would never get anything done! Hashem designed the heart as an involuntary muscle. This means it tightens and expands as needed, without you consciously telling it to. Even as you sleep, it beats on rhythm to keep you functioning.

When Hashem gives us a gift, we must act responsibly and take good care of it. Here are some ways you can keep your heart healthy.

- Be physically active in a way that gets you huffing and puffing. The recommended amount of time is 30-60 minutes a day.
- Eat fruits, vegetables, and healthy grains.
- Avoid junk food, sweet drinks, and unhealthy fats.
- Avoid breathing smoky, polluted air.

Let's Talk About It
Can you think of another wonderful feature of your awesome heart?

See page 252 for possible answers.

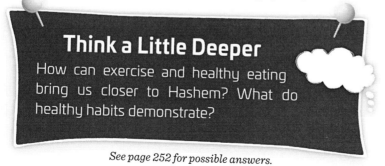

Think a Little Deeper
How can exercise and healthy eating bring us closer to Hashem? What do healthy habits demonstrate?

See page 252 for possible answers.

Great People, Great *Emunah*

Rav Asher Druk heard of a man in Israel who was traveling to America to get an artificial heart transplant. The procedure was going to cost about a million dollars. The Rabbi took a valuable lesson from this. "If an artificial heart is worth a million dollars," he said, "how much is a real heart worth?"

82
CAPTURED BY A PICTURE

The Przewozman family in Eretz Yisrael was sitting *shivah* for their son, Pinchas Menachem *Hy"d*, who had lost his life in a terror attack.

Relatives, friends, and strangers traveled from all over the country to be with the family in their time of pain. Among them stood a gentleman named Levi. He appeared to be especially shaken up. He made his way toward the front of the room and sat on a chair facing the mourners.

Levi handed Pinchas Menachem's father a photo album. He explained, "I am a photographer. I met your son briefly about six months ago. My partner and I were on an early morning expedition to capture the sunrise. As we hiked along a nature path carrying our cameras and equipment, we noticed a beautiful, touching scene."

Levi paused and swallowed a lump in his throat. "We saw a group of Chassidic young men preparing to pray Shacharis. One of them, your son, was wearing his *tallis* and *tefillin*. I approached him and requested permission to photograph him. He was very pleasant to talk to and agreed to be photographed. We took some dramatic photos, and then we parted ways."

The photographer opened the album and showed some pictures to the family. Pinchas Menachem's father pointed to one of the photos. It was a close-up of Pinchas Menachem wrapped in his *tallis* and *tefillin,* with a pure, angelic face.

He turned to Levi and said, "I want you to know that because of this picture, Jews have returned to the mitzvah of *tefillin.*"

Levi was stunned. "What are you talking about?"

The father explained. "After the attack, all the newspapers and media outlets carried this very picture, which you captured that morning in the forest. Jews of all backgrounds felt an instant connection to our son and the spirituality in the photo. Over the last few days, we have heard that because of this picture, several individuals have committed to start wearing *tefillin.*"

Let's Talk About It

Can you find the *hashgachah pratis* in this story?

See page 252 for possible answers.

Think a Little Deeper

Levi took the picture six months before it became famous. Do you think he ever imagined it would bring Jews back to the mitzvah of *tefillin*? Hashem is behind everything. There is no such thing as a "chance meeting."

It Happened to Me!

What is YOUR *hashgachah pratis* story?

Can you think of a time when you found yourself in exactly the right place, at exactly the right moment?

83
THANK YOU, HASHEM, AGAIN AND AGAIN

Mr. Charlie Harary had a good friend who was making a wedding in Miami. The wedding was set for a Thursday evening. Mr. Harary was scheduled to deliver a speech in Chicago the day before, so he made sure to book tickets that would allow him to get to the wedding in time.

He arrived at the airport bright and early. But when he checked the signs for departure times, he saw that his flight was delayed.

Oh no, he thought. *I really don't want to miss this wedding!*

When he checked the signs again, the posted departure time was even later.

Mr. Harary contacted the airline to see if there was anything they could do. He told them how important it was for him to be in Miami that night and asked if they could arrange an alternate flight.

"I'm sorry," the airline representative said. "Today is one of the busiest travel days of the entire year. All other options are booked solid."

Let's Talk About It

Picture yourself in this situation. Think: How would Hashem want me to react?

See page 252 for possible answers.

Mr. Harary was understandably upset. But then he remembered a story he had heard a few weeks before.

A woman who had been childless approached her Rabbi. "We have tried everything possible to be blessed with children. It seems like only Hashem Himself can help. How can I merit more Heavenly help?"

The Rabbi asked, "Did you ever thank Hashem for not giving you children?"

The woman was surprised. "Why would I do that?" she asked. "I want children more than anything!"

The Rabbi explained, "We believe that Hashem does everything for the best. If He hasn't given you children until now, you should thank Him for that. Keep praying to have children in the future, but also thank Hashem that you don't have children right now."

The woman took the Rabbi's words to heart and by the end of that year, she merited to hold her very own child.

As Mr. Harary stood in the airport and thought about the message of this story, he challenged himself to do the same.

With great courage, he said, "Hashem, You know what's best for me better than I do. I thought I need to be in Miami tonight, but You caused my flight to get delayed. It must be that missing the wedding is the best possible outcome for me, so I'm going to thank You for it."

He then closed his eyes and said, "Thank You, Hashem, for delaying my flight." He repeated these words over and over with great concentration.

After about twenty times, he began to feel much calmer. He believed what he was saying and found that he was not so upset anymore. He even hoped for a miracle. Maybe the airline would contact him and say they found him a seat on another flight… But that never happened. Nobody called. He was left with no choice but to fly back to New York.

Mr. Harary went to work as usual. Throughout the day, whenever he felt a twinge of regret, he would say, "Thank You, Hashem, for arranging that I miss the wedding." And so he went through a regular day of work instead of celebrating with his close friend.

When he arrived home, his wife had an interesting message for him.

"Somebody came by before and dropped off this package for you," she said. Mr. Harary was curious. He was not expecting any deliveries. He opened the box and was overwhelmed by its contents. It was full of magnets, stickers, wristbands, and hats… *and every single item had the words "Thank You, Hashem"!*

Think a Little Deeper
What message was Hashem sending Mr. Harary?

See page 252 for possible answers.

84
THE WINNING TICKET

*Y*israel worked in a small office with several other Jewish men. But no matter how hard he tried, he struggled to make ends meet. His coworkers seemed to be much more successful.

One day, the people in the office decided to purchase lottery tickets. Yisrael also bought one. Then he had an idea.

Meir has all the luck around here, he thought. *I will switch my lottery ticket with his.*

He felt guilty about being dishonest, but he was overpowered by the desire to finally make some money. When Meir wasn't looking, Yisrael took the ticket from his desk and swapped it for his own.

A few days later, the winning numbers were announced. Imagine Yisrael's shock when Meir was declared the winner! The numbers Yisrael had traded away were an exact match! All he had to show for himself was a worthless piece of paper.

Let's Talk About It

Yisrael was deeply disappointed because he felt that by exchanging his ticket for Meir's, he had lost a lot of money. Look at the situation with "emunah glasses." Do you see anything different?

See page 252 for possible answers.

Yisrael was filled with pain and regret. He considered approaching Meir and explaining what had happened. But first he decided to ask Rav Chaim Kanievsky if he had any right to claim the money.

Rav Chaim's response was clear. The money belonged to Meir. "Tickets don't win lotteries," he said. "People do. The ticket you have doesn't matter. If a person is supposed to win, Hashem will make him win."

Rav Chaim also said over something he had heard from the Chazon Ish. A plane had crashed, and the Chazon Ish said, "It's not a plane that crashes, it's the people that crash. If there is even one person on a plane that is not supposed to crash, the plane will not go down."

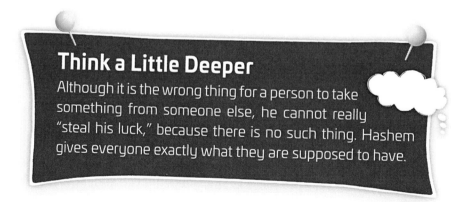

Think a Little Deeper

Although it is the wrong thing for a person to take something from someone else, he cannot really "steal his luck," because there is no such thing. Hashem gives everyone exactly what they are supposed to have.

85
IN THE BLINK OF AN EYE

abbi Shalom Mordechai Rubashkin is famous for his unshakeable *emunah* and *bitachon*. When he was arrested and imprisoned with a 27-year-sentence, he never lost his belief in Hashem. He worked with top lawyers and community activists to expedite his release, but he always remembered that Hashem was the only One he could rely upon.

Rabbi Rubashkin began every day in prison by reciting the entire *sefer Tehillim*. One day, after eight years in prison, a prison guard entered his cell.

"You have official mail," said the guard. It was from the US Appeals Court. Rabbi Rubashkin was hopeful. His lawyers had worked with the Appeals Court for several months. Perhaps inside he would find good news? The Rabbi opened the envelope.

The paper contained one word: "Denied." It appeared that his last chance was gone.

Let's Talk About It

What could have been Rabbi Rubashkin's natural reaction? How do you think Hashem wanted him to react?

See page 252 for possible answers.

The Rabbi held the paper in his hands and closed his eyes.

"Hashem, this letter is from the court system down here on earth," he prayed. "You are bigger than this, and Your power is way stronger than even the highest court in the country. You can create a miracle for me even with this denial."

Despite the difficult news, the Rabbi's spirit was not crushed. The next morning was the last day of Chanukah. Rabbi Rubashkin began his day with *Tehillim*, just like every day.

"Hashem," he cried, "I believe with my entire being that You can release me any day You choose, even today!" The Rabbi prepared to celebrate the last day of Chanukah with a special joyous feast.

Think a Little Deeper

How do you think Rabbi Rubashkin was able to muster up *emunah* and *bitachon* even after hearing such crushing news?

See page 252 for possible answers.

Rabbi Rubashkin wryly describes his meal that morning: "First I washed, and I ate matzah and tuna fish. Then I had more tuna fish with matzah. And for the third course, I had matzah with tuna fish again..." This was all he had, yet he sang to Hashem with a heart full of love. In the midst of his modest Chanukah meal, a guard opened the door.

"You are being transferred to a new location," he said.

Rabbi Rubashkin was led to an office and handed another envelope. Inside was a declaration from the president of the United States that he was free to go home.

In one instant, all his prayers, *emunah,* and *bitachon* of eight long years were answered.

That night, thousands of Jews surrounded the Rubashkin home in song and dance, celebrating the great miracle that had come about with so much *emunah* and *bitachon.*

A Family of *Baalei Emunah*

Rabbi Shalom Mordechai's wife is also well known for her steadfast *emunah* and *bitachon.* Even while her husband was imprisoned, she would go around to schools and community centers speaking of belief and trust in Hashem. Throughout those years, Mrs. Rubashkin always kept a set of her husband's clothing in her car. "We really believed Hashem could release him at any moment," she said. Mrs. Rubashkin demonstrated her belief that יְשׁוּעַת הַשֵּׁם כְּהֶרֶף עַיִן, the salvation of Hashem comes in the blink of an eye.

86
WIN-WIN

An impala was peacefully grazing in the morning sun. A type of bird known as the oxpecker flew down, landed on the impala's head, and began pecking at its ear.

Sounds strange? This is actually a common sight on the African savanna, where oxpeckers can be found on buffalo, giraffes, impalas, and other large animals. Perched on their host animals, oxpeckers feast on ticks, fleas, lice, and other bugs.

Hashem designed this remarkable relationship to benefit both the host animal and the bird. Insects can cause infection and disease, and the oxpecker is a convenient form of pest control. The oxpecker gains by having an endless supply of nourishment. Both the host animal and oxpecker are protected by the bird's natural warning system against predators. When it senses danger, it lets out a loud warning call. This allows the animal and bird to escape in time.

Let's Talk About It

What does this have to do with us? How can discussing amazing wonders in the animal world increase our *emunah*?

See page 253 for possible answers.

A similar relationship exists between remora fish and sharks. Remora are small fish that have a special front dorsal fin that hooks onto passing sharks and whales. Remora service these large marine animals by cleaning their skin from parasites. Sharks even allow these fish to enter their mouths and clean leftover food from their teeth. In exchange, the remora fish get free meals, transportation, and protection from the shark.

These mutually beneficial partnerships exist among many animals and fish. They are examples of Hashem's perfection and exactitude.

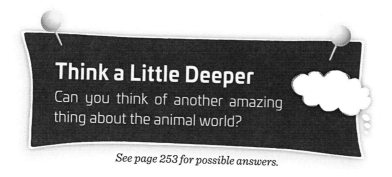

Think a Little Deeper

Can you think of another amazing thing about the animal world?

See page 253 for possible answers.

87
ODD NUMBER, BREAKING EVEN

Shimon's financial situation was not good. He felt bad doing so, but with no other choice, he and his wife approached people in the community for help. Fortunately, his wife was able to get in touch with a generous woman who really got the family back on their feet.

Shimon was now able to pay his bills independently, but he did not forget how hard it was to be on the receiving end. He made a point of giving as much *tzedakah* as possible.

During one pre-Pesach season, Shimon was approached by a Jew in need. He gladly gave him $180. The same day, he made a $170 donation to his shul. Shortly after that, he heard of two worthy organizations that were raising funds to help families make Pesach. He extended himself to give them $500 each.

Shimon was on a high. Even though he

wasn't exactly rolling in extra cash, he was grateful to be able to give. He came home to his wife and said, "I had such a successful week! I was able to give $1,350 to *tzedakah*."

"You are not going to believe this," she replied. "Remember that special woman who helped us out when we were struggling? She called to let me know that as a holiday present, she deposited $1,300 dollars into our grocery account."

That night, Shimon's wife contacted the woman to thank her for the surprise gift. She asked what significance there was to the amount $1300.

"I'm not really sure," the woman said. "It's a random number, I know. That's just what popped into my head."

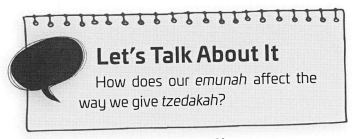

Let's Talk About It

How does our *emunah* affect the way we give *tzedakah*?

See page 253 for possible answers.

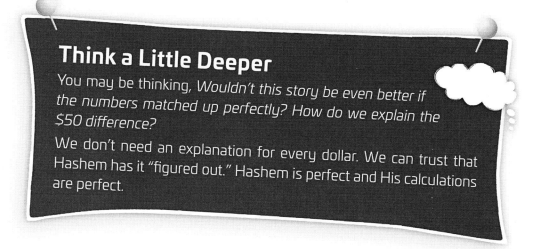

Think a Little Deeper

You may be thinking, *Wouldn't this story be even better if the numbers matched up perfectly? How do we explain the $50 difference?*

We don't need an explanation for every dollar. We can trust that Hashem has it "figured out." Hashem is perfect and His calculations are perfect.

88
A COOL INVENTION

Can you imagine a world without ice cream?

Ice cream is a delicious treat. It is sweet, cool, and refreshing. It enhances *siyumim,* birthday parties, and hot summer days. But do we really need ice cream in order to survive? In the days before it was created, do you think people managed?

Let's Talk About It

Of course we could have managed without ice cream. Yet Hashem gave it to us as a delightful, pleasurable treat. Why do you think He did so?

See page 253 for possible answers.

Hashem created the world in order to give us ultimate good. Hashem gave us Torah and mitzvos to bring us closer to Him. But Hashem did us a huge *chesed*. He made our lives pleasant by adding in all these little treats along the way, like popcorn, pickles... and ice cream!

If you are not used to doing so, it may feel silly to say, "Thank You, Hashem, for this yummy ice cream." But it's the truth; Hashem created it especially for your enjoyment! Not only did He bless you with ice cream, He gave you sprinkles, syrup, and a convenient cone to hold it all.

There is some disagreement over who gets the credit for inventing the first ice-cream cone. According to one version, a waffle vendor and an ice-cream vendor stood side by side at a fair. The ice-cream seller was running out of dishes so the waffle man twisted one of his waffles into the shape of a cone. When it hardened, it served as the perfect holder for ice cream. The customers liked it and the crispy cone became a popular item.

When we look at this story with *"emunah* glasses," we can easily find Hashem. Clearly it was time for the ice-cream cone to enter the world. Through this amazing setup between the two vendors, Hashem allowed it to be introduced.

Imagine how this way of thinking will affect your ice cream-eating experience. As you hold a drippy cone in your hand, you will feel a surge of love and thanks to the Creator of this marvelous invention, and you will say, "Thank You, Hashem, for this delicious ice cream and nifty cone!" Like all yummy foods, it is just another way through which we can connect to Hashem.

Think a Little Deeper
What other delicious "extras" can you thank Hashem for?

See page 253 for possible answers.

89
PRECIOUS LASHES

At the edge of a small town, in a tiny little shack, lived Moshke the innkeeper. He operated his inn in the front portion of the hut and his family lived in the back. He was supposed to pay rent to the wealthy landowner on a monthly basis, but the little inn rarely brought in enough money. Fortunately, his landowner was an easygoing fellow and never said a word about it.

One year, the landowner had to travel far away on business. He appointed his caretaker to manage his properties while he was gone. Unfortunately, the caretaker was not quite as nice as his boss. In fact, he was known to be very mean. On the day that Moshke's rent was due, he marched straight up to the inn.

"Open up!" he barked. "Hand over the money!"

Moshke appeared in the doorway, trembling with fear.

"I d-d-don't have any m-m-money," he stammered.

The cruel caretaker dragged Moshke out to the street and began beating him. The innkeeper cried in pain as he felt each lash on his back. One, two, three... ten lashes and the caretaker was satisfied.

"If you will not pay up next month, you can expect the same treatment," he sneered.

Moshke staggered home and collapsed into bed. For several days, the inn remained closed while he recuperated.

When the beginning of the next month rolled around, Moshke simply had no money. The caretaker repeated his brutal treatment. This went on for many months. The poor innkeeper prayed for the day that the landowner would return.

Eventually, the kind and patient landowner did indeed return. Moshke approached him and shared what had happened while he was away.

"I cannot allow such behavior to go unpunished," announced the landowner. "The caretaker must pay you ten gold coins for every time he hit you."

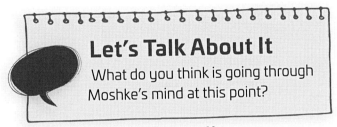

Let's Talk About It
What do you think is going through Moshke's mind at this point?

See page 253 for possible answers.

Moshke's face fell.

"What's wrong now?" the landowner asked.

The innkeeper moaned. "If I would have only known that I would get paid for each of those lashes, I would not have complained; I would have let him hit me even more."

Think a Little Deeper
What should a person think while going through a difficult ordeal?

See page 253 for possible answers.

90

A PLEA FROM THE HEART

It was late at night when a father of twin boys arrived at the Beilinson Hospital in Israel. One of his sons was very ill and was scheduled for surgery the next morning. Near the hospital stood a building where patients could rest the night before an early procedure.

The boy went to sleep right away in order to have strength for the next day. His father was too anxious to fall asleep. He decided to go for a walk around the building.

Outside, he paced the grounds, worrying about his child. As he walked in the cool night air, he noticed the entrance to a small shul. He was not religious, but in his worried state, he felt pulled toward the little shul.

Inside, it was dark. A faint glow emanated from the *ner tamid*. The man sat down and started to cry. He found a *Tehillim* on a nearby table and recited the words with a broken heart.

He prayed for hours, tears streaming down his face. He came across the words שַׁוְעָתִי אֵלֶיךָ וַתִּרְפָּאֵנִי, a request for healing. He begged Hashem to have mercy and heal his child. Then he went back to the room and fell asleep beside his son.

Let's Talk About It
How does praying for the sick show *emunah*?

See page 253 for possible answers.

The next morning, father and son went to the hospital for one last scan before the procedure. The doctor needed to assess the situation before operating. The test took a long while. When it was complete, the doctor reviewed the results and shook his head.

"It didn't come out clear," he said. "We have to do it again."

The scan was repeated, but again, the images were unclear.

"We will do it one more time from a different angle," the doctor said.

After the third scan, the doctor called the father into his office. He held up the papers showing the results of all three tests and said, "I have no idea how to explain this. I don't see any sign of the disease. I know this boy has a twin brother. Are you sure this is the patient?"

The father began to cry tears of joy. He thought back to his heartfelt prayers in the dark shul. He hugged his son tightly and whispered a prayer of thanks to Hashem.

Think a Little Deeper
How can *tefillah* take away sickness?

See page 253 for possible answers.

91
SYMPTOMS OF LOVE

"Mommy, I'm not feeling well." Shmuel's cheeks were red and his eyes drooped. His mother pressed a hand to his forehead.

"You are warm, my dear. I think you might have fever." Shmuel's mother led him to the couch and helped him find a comfortable position. "Your body needs plenty of rest and lots of fluids. Hopefully that will bring down your temperature."

Shmuel drank a warm tea and fell asleep on the couch. When he woke up, he made sure to drink some more. By the end of the day, he still did not feel better.

His mother took his temperature again. "Tomorrow I will take you to see the doctor," she said.

The next day, the doctor checked Shmuel's eyes and ears. He used a special swab to test Shmuel's throat for infection.

"It seems like you have strep," the doctor said. "I am going to send a prescription to the pharmacy. Your mother will give you medicine and with Hashem's help, you'll feel better very soon."

Shmuel thanked the kind doctor and followed his mother into the car.

"*Baruch Hashem* we caught it early," his mother said. "Your aches and pains were warning signs that your body is fighting an infection. That's how we knew that you needed to rest."

Shmuel thought about this. "I was feeling achy and sleepy. My body hurt. But because of the fever, we knew to go to the doctor. Now I will have the proper medicine to help take care of the problem."

"Exactly right!" his mother said. "Hashem designed our bodies with a special warning system that lets us know when something needs extra care. If a person feels pain, it's a sign that he needs to look into it and help his body heal."

Shmuel yawned tiredly. Then he smiled. "I thought the fever was just bothersome and annoying, but really it's a gift from Hashem."

Let's Talk About It

Infections inside the body would remain a mystery without outward symptoms. Although nobody enjoys feeling pain, it is really our body's special way of telling us that something is not right.

Think a Little Deeper

Symptoms of illness are a sign of Hashem's love. How can we use this knowledge to strengthen our *emunah*?

See page 253 for possible answers.

92
JUST IN TIME

Yonah was driving along a narrow road. A Torah class was playing from the car's speakers. As he drove, he kept his eyes on his lane, carefully following its twists and turns.

Right behind Yonah's car was a large jeep. The driver was impatient and decided to pass Yonah on the left. He started to accelerate and was about to pass Yonah's car. Yonah did not realize this. In fact, at that very moment, he noticed his own car was too far to the right and figured he would steer slightly toward the left.

As he was about to move his car directly into the jeep's path, Yonah heard a loud honk. He grabbed the wheel and steadied his car just in time. The jeep roared past Yonah's left side and a major collision was averted.

With a pounding heart, Yonah slowed down to process what had just happened. He was grateful to be alive.

I wonder where that honk came from, he thought. It did not sound like it came from the jeep.

Yonah calmed down and rewound the CD to the part he was listening to before the scare. He focused on the Torah class when suddenly he heard a car beeping in the background. It was coming from the recording! The jeep had never honked at all. The sound had come from within Yonah's own car.

That honk saved my life! Yonah realized.

Let's Talk About It

Where in this story do we see Hashem's involvement?

See page 253 for possible answers.

Think a Little Deeper

This story actually has multiple layers of *hashgachah pratis*. Way before Yonah's trip, when the Torah class was originally recorded, Hashem orchestrated that a car would honk in the background. This sound became part of the CD, and much later on, Yonah heard it at precisely the right moment.

It Happened to Me!

What is YOUR *hashgachah pratis* story? Share something that happened to you this week. See if you can find another layer of *hashgachah*, like in Yonah's story.

93
SMOOTHING OVER THE CRACKS

Yehoshua beamed as he opened the box of his brand-new ripstick. His grandparents had bought it for him as an *afikoman* gift, and now on Chol HaMoed, he was excited to try it out.

Within minutes, Yehoshua was expertly weaving through the parked cars in his grandparents' spacious driveway. All day, he rode his new toy, perfecting his balance and trying out new turns.

"Thank you, Grandma! Thank you, Grandpa!" he said as he popped into the house for a drink. "This is the best gift ever!"

After Yom Tov, Yehoshua's family loaded up the car for their trip back to Monsey, where they lived.

"I'll hold my ripstick the entire way," Yehoshua called out. Everyone smiled. He was clearly excited about this *afikoman* gift.

When they arrived home, Yehoshua realized he had a problem. Their driveway was not as straight as his grandparents' driveway. He tried riding on the street, but it was full of cracks.

Let's Talk About It

Picture yourself in this situation. How would Hashem want you to react?

See page 254 for possible answers.

"I can't ride my ripstick here," he moaned. "The pavement is all broken!" His mother decided to turn the situation into an *emunah* moment.

"Hashem does everything for our best," she said. "Let's thank Him that you were able to use it at Grandma and Grandpa's house. We can also thank Hashem that you can't use it here, because if our driveway is hilly and the street here is cracked, it's for our best."

Yehoshua accepted his mother's wise words and thanked Hashem. That night, while he slept, servicemen posted "No Parking" signs all along the street. In the morning, three humongous, noisy trucks pulled up and repaved half the street; it was the side of the block that Yehoshua's family lived on.

After school, Yehoshua skipped happily into the house to get his ripstick. And as he rode on the beautiful, fresh pavement, he whispered, "Thank You, Hashem, thank you!"

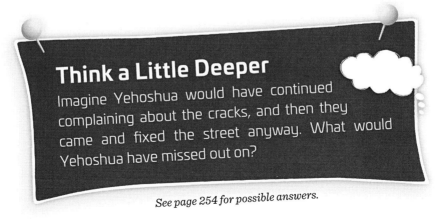

Think a Little Deeper

Imagine Yehoshua would have continued complaining about the cracks, and then they came and fixed the street anyway. What would Yehoshua have missed out on?

See page 254 for possible answers.

94
THE JUDGE IS...

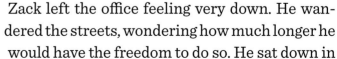

*Z*ack was a Jewish kid who was raised secular. Unfortunately, he got involved in crime at a young age. By the time he was in his twenties, he was making a lot of money from illegal activities.

One day, he sat in an upscale restaurant closing another one of his shady deals. He was not aware that the FBI was watching and recording every move. As soon as the FBI had enough evidence, they snapped handcuffs onto Zack and arrested him.

Zack was crushed. He posted bail and consulted with a top lawyer. The lawyer's response was not encouraging. "You have a lot going against you," he said. "The FBI has everything on tape. I will do my best, but don't get your hopes up."

Zack left the office feeling very down. He wandered the streets, wondering how much longer he would have the freedom to do so. He sat down in a diner, tears pouring down his face. He cried and cried.

An older fellow watched through the window. He came in and sat near Zack, putting his arm around his shoulder. "You look troubled," he said. "Something must be very wrong. What is the problem?"

"What do you know about problems?!" Zack responded angrily.

The older man rolled up his sleeve and revealed numbers tattooed onto his arm. He was a Holocaust survivor. "I know a lot about problems," he said softly. "Let me help you."

Zack told the man he was also Jewish. He shared his story with all its details. The man listened to every word and said, "You need to speak with a Rabbi; come with me."

Together they went to the Skolya Rebbe. The Rebbe listened and gave Zack a *berachah,* telling him not to worry.

"Everything will be fine," the Rebbe said reassuringly. "Go to court. Your lawyer will be late, but don't panic. You are going to win."

On the day of the trial, Zack arrived at court exactly on time. When he saw the FBI agents who had arrested him, he started to sweat. His fate would be determined in the next few hours.

As the Rebbe had predicted, his lawyer was late. He called Zack to say he had missed his flight and was sending a replacement.

When Zack saw the replacement, he thought he would faint. The lawyer was a young rookie with barely any court experience. Zack covered his face in despair.

Let's Talk About It
How can a situation as desperate as this still be for the best?

See page 254 for possible answers.

The judge called the court to order and began the proceedings. The prosecution made their case and presented the evidence. Then the young lawyer got up to speak in Zack's defense.

For the first few minutes he was on target, but after that he went totally off. No one knew what he was talking about. The lawyer spoke gibberish for nearly an hour. Zack slid lower and lower in his seat. When the rookie was done, the judge turned to the prosecution.

"It's clear you don't have enough evidence against Zack," he said. "This case is dismissed."

Zack stumbled to his feet in shock. Was he really a free man? He went over to thank the young lawyer.

"I thought I was doomed," he said. "How did you pull that off?"

The lawyer smiled. "This is my first case," he replied. "But the judge is my grandpa."

Zack returned to the Skolya Rebbe, who encouraged him to begin putting on *tefillin* every day. He left his crooked ways and slowly became religious. He raised a beautiful family of G-d-fearing children and grandchildren.

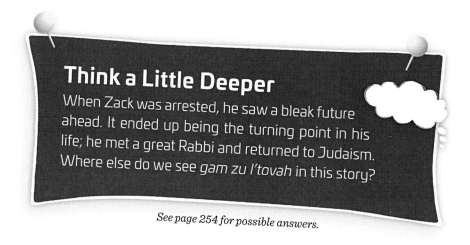

Think a Little Deeper

When Zack was arrested, he saw a bleak future ahead. It ended up being the turning point in his life; he met a great Rabbi and returned to Judaism. Where else do we see *gam zu l'tovah* in this story?

See page 254 for possible answers.

95
FROM THE HEART

Every Thursday night, Moshe would prepare money for his wife to buy food for Shabbos. One Thursday, he had no money at all to give her. He did not want to frighten his wife or children. Instead, he went into his study and turned to Hashem.

"Hashem, You take care of all Your creations. You are in charge of all the food in the world, and You can provide for my family this week just like any other." Moshe spoke straight from his heart, expressing his deep faith and trust that Hashem could change the situation in a moment.

When he came out of the room, he found an entire Shabbos meal on the kitchen table.

"Where did all this food come from?" Moshe asked in wonder.

"Our neighbor's daughter had a baby boy," his wife said. "They are traveling out of town for the *shalom zachar*. They already finished cooking for Shabbos and didn't want all this to go to waste."

Let's Talk About It

Hashem can do anything. Hashem can give us anything. Why does He sometimes wait for us to ask?

See page 254 for possible answers.

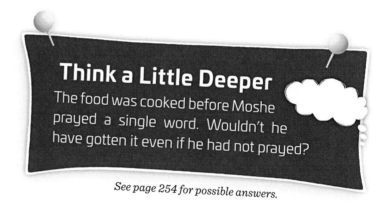

Think a Little Deeper

The food was cooked before Moshe prayed a single word. Wouldn't he have gotten it even if he had not prayed?

See page 254 for possible answers.

Great People, Great *Emunah*

When the Ksav Sofer was the Rabbi of the city of Pressburg, a Jew was falsely accused of a crime and sentenced to hanging. The Ksav Sofer worked with prominent individuals to petition in court, but nothing could save the condemned man. The night before the scheduled execution, the Ksav Sofer came home exhausted, broken and distressed. With nothing left to do, he sat in his chair and cried himself to sleep.

As he slept, his father, the Chasam Sofer, appeared to him in a dream with an angry face.

"How are you able to sleep," the Chasam Sofer said, "when an innocent man with a wife and children is going to be put to death?"

"But what should I do?" the Ksav Sofer asked his father in the dream. "I've already tried everything."

"Why aren't you praying?" his father asked. "You have to pray, pray, and pray some more."

The Ksav Sofer immediately arose and gathered the community to the synagogue for prayer. In a broken voice, he cried to the townspeople, "We have tried everything we could, but all the doors are locked. The gates of tears, however, are never locked. Hashem can still help." The people cried and prayed throughout the rest of the night.

When morning came, the judge miraculously agreed to investigate the case further. The man was declared innocent and his life was saved.

96
TAP, TAP, TAP

ap, tap, tap! Something is making a racket up there in the trees. Chances are, it's a woodpecker! Woodpeckers are a type of bird found all over the world. They peck about 20 times per second, and between 8,000 and 12,000 times per day. Their noisy, trademark way of pecking at wood earned them their name.

Hashem created these birds with everything they need for their unique way of life. A woodpecker's pointed beak acts as a two-in-one crowbar and chisel. It can hammer open wood and pry out insects that live inside. Once a woodpecker has drilled a hole in a tree, its long, sticky tongue helps it reach its food.

As you can imagine, all that pecking creates quite a mess. Woodpeckers have a special membrane that covers their eyes a millisecond before the beak comes in contact with wood. This protects their eyes from flying debris. They also have tiny feathers covering their nostrils, preventing them from inhaling sawdust as they peck away.

Woodpeckers have other unique features too. Their feet have four toes each, two facing forward and two facing back. This helps them walk straight up tree trunks, and gives them a steady grip on branches. Stiff tail feathers keep them propped in place on tree trunks.

You might wonder how the constant banging and shaking affects the little bird's brain. If a typical bird would move its head so rapidly, it would suffer a concussion. A woodpecker's skull has a spongy material in it that absorbs shock. There is also a special bone that keeps the brain from moving around.

Who designed such a perfect creature? Who can possibly think of all these details? It can only be Hashem!

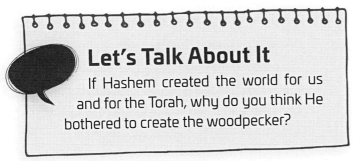

Let's Talk About It

If Hashem created the world for us and for the Torah, why do you think He bothered to create the woodpecker?

See page 254 for possible answers.

Think a Little Deeper

What *emunah* lesson can we learn by observing the woodpecker?

See page 254 for possible answers.

97
PERFECT PAYBACK

Efraim was learning in a yeshivah in Israel. One afternoon, he was in a hurry to get home. Instead of taking the bus, he flagged down a taxi and got in. He decided to use his time in the car to review the Gemara he was learning.

Soon Efraim arrived at his destination. He was so engrossed in his learning that he exited the cab without paying. The driver realized that his passenger had made an honest mistake. He decided to ignore it and zipped off to find his next customer.

Suddenly, Efraim stopped in his tracks.

"Oh, no! I forgot to pay the driver," he realized.

Efraim spun around and began chasing the taxi. He ran as fast as he could. He chased it from one corner to the next. Every time the taxi stopped at a red light, Efraim thought he'd catch it.

But the light turned green and the taxi continued driving.

Finally, Efraim caught up. Totally out of breath, he knocked on the window and the driver rolled it down.

"I forgot to pay you," Efraim panted. "I'm so sorry! Here's the money."

The driver was shocked. "What?! You chased me all the way here?" He could not believe that Efraim had run so far just to pay him.

Thirty years passed.

Efraim noticed a sign in his shul saying that a famous Rabbi would be speaking about *kiddush Hashem*. It sounded interesting and he decided to attend.

The Rabbi spoke beautifully. He explained that when someone makes a *kiddush Hashem*, Hashem lets that person see all the great things that happened because of it.

After the speech, Efraim approached the Rabbi and asked, "Thirty years ago I made a *kiddush Hashem* and I haven't seen anything happen because of it." He told the Rabbi about how he had chased the taxi driver in order to pay him.

The Rabbi heard the story and shouted, "I cannot believe this. I am that driver!"

He told Efraim, "When I saw how honest a yeshivah *bachur* was, I decided to become religious myself. I started learning and I became a Rabbi all because of you! Right now, Hashem is showing you the powerful effect of your mitzvah."

Let's Talk About It
Where in this story do we clearly see *hashgachah pratis*?

See page 254 for possible answers.

Think a Little Deeper

What can we learn from the fact that it took Efraim so many years to see the results of his *kiddush Hashem?*

See page 254 for possible answers.

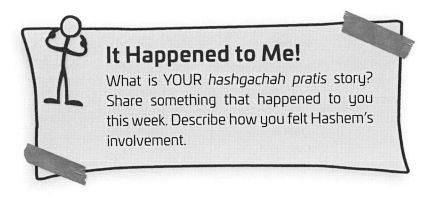

It Happened to Me!

What is YOUR *hashgachah pratis* story? Share something that happened to you this week. Describe how you felt Hashem's involvement.

98
FOR
PROBLEMS TOO

Many years ago, there lived a simple Jew named Berel. Berel was a chassid who hoped and dreamed to visit his Rebbe, the Chozeh of Lublin. For many months he carefully set aside money until he had enough funds to make the journey.

After a long and tiring trip, Berel arrived in Lublin. He entered the room of the Chozeh with great trepidation and awe.

The Chozeh took one look at Berel and said, "Return home, at once!"

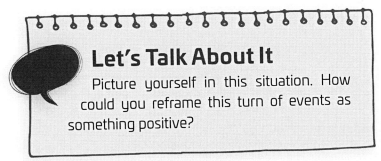

Let's Talk About It

Picture yourself in this situation. How could you reframe this turn of events as something positive?

See page 255 for possible answers.

Berel was dumbfounded. He had traveled so long and so far, only to be sent back after barely arriving. Not one to challenge the words of his holy Rebbe, Berel immediately set out on the road toward his hometown.

That night, he stopped off at an inn where he met a merry group of chassidim.

"Berel," said one of them, "why don't you join us? We are going to see the great Chozeh of Lublin."

Berel looked down dejectedly. "I actually just left Lublin earlier today," he said. "I spent several months making arrangements for this trip, but after seeing me for just a moment, the Rebbe sent me back home."

"Why are you so down?" the chassidim asked him. "If this is what happened, it must be Hashem's will! There is no reason to feel so down if you are doing what Hashem wants you to do."

The chassidim proceeded to make a festive meal in Berel's honor.

One of them got up to speak. "Tonight we celebrate the loving acceptance of Hashem's will by our dear friend Berel!" he announced. The men sang and danced straight through the night and sure enough, Berel's spirits were uplifted. He was able to feel a deep sense of peace and happiness, even though his trip had not gone according to plan.

The next morning, the chassidim told Berel, "Now you are able to return with us to the Rebbe."

Berel joined the group and traveled back to Lublin.

When the Rebbe saw him, he was amazed. "What happened to you?" he asked.

Berel told the Rebbe about the celebration in the inn.

"Incredible!" the Rebbe said. "When you were here yesterday, I saw a Heavenly decree of death against you, and so I instructed you to return home so you could die peacefully, surrounded by your family. But because you accepted Hashem's will with such faith and joy, the decree was annulled."

Think a Little Deeper

Emunah and *bitachon* are so powerful, they can actually overturn an evil decree.

99

A GOLDEN OPPORTUNITY

Manny Hoff worked in the gold business. He would purchase used jewelry that people no longer needed and resell it to dealers for a profit.

Manny had several loyal customers that he kept in touch with over the years. One of them was Mr. Black.

One day, Mr. Black contacted Manny and said, "I have a large amount of gold that I would like to sell at a great price." The two men discussed the details and agreed to finalize the sale later on in the day.

Before Manny went to pick up the gold, he called Mr. Black to see if he was home.

"Actually, I just sold it all to another dealer," he said.

Let's Talk About It

Picture yourself in this situation. Think:
How would Hashem want me to react?

See page 255 for possible answers.

Manny was devastated. *How could he do this to me?* he thought. *We had a deal!*

But Manny was a G-d-fearing Jew. He spent a few moments reminding himself that everything Hashem does is for the good.

It must be that this deal was never meant for me in the first place, he thought to himself. He even resolved to judge Mr. Black favorably and forgive him for giving the business to someone else.

A few moments later, he checked the predicted price of gold for the next morning. To his amazement, the numbers showed the largest price drop he had ever seen. He had just been prevented from suffering a huge loss.

He called his Rabbi excitedly and said, "I have a great *hashgachah pratis* story to share with you." He then told him what happened.

Manny was still in a good mood when he rechecked the predicted rate later in the day. There was a notice that said there had been a glitch in the system and the price of gold was not dropping after all.

Manny called back his Rabbi with the update.

"I guess it's not such a great *hashgachah* story after all," he sighed.

The Rabbi responded, "Actually, now it's an even better story. Hashem's involvement then and now is exactly the same. He made sure the sale didn't go through for you, and that is *still* the best possible outcome!"

Think a Little Deeper

It is a great level of *emunah* to see one thing and believe something else. To Manny's logical mind, his customer caused him financial loss. But in fact, everything Hashem does is for our ultimate gain. Manny was presented with a golden opportunity to serve Hashem by believing that this apparent "loss" was really for his benefit.

100
HASHEM
SAID, "NO."

It was Motzaei Yom Kippur in the city of Lublin. The shul's congregants were about to leave when the Chozeh of Lublin made an astonishing announcement.

"If anyone would like, I can tell them exactly what they prayed for this year."

The people were taken aback. They looked nervously at one another, but it didn't seem like anybody was brave enough to take up the unusual offer.

Finally, one man came forward and said, "Would the Rabbi tell me what I prayed for?"

"You really struggled to learn Torah this past year," the Chozeh began. "You spent most of your day working hard to support your family. When you came home, you hurriedly ate dinner so you could go back out to learn. You managed to learn for only one hour a night."

The Chozeh concluded, "You prayed for an easier schedule so you could learn Torah for longer periods of time and with greater peace of mind."

"Yes, yes!" the man exclaimed. "That is exactly what I prayed for. What was Hashem's response?"

"Hashem said, 'No,'" the Chozeh replied.

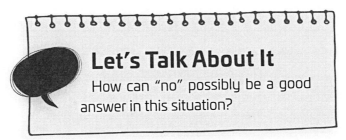

Let's Talk About It
How can "no" possibly be a good answer in this situation?

See page 255 for possible answers.

The man was shocked and disappointed.

In a pained voice, he asked, "All I want is to learn more Torah and serve Hashem better. Why would Hashem deny such a request?"

The Chozeh explained, "The way you struggle to learn now, with such difficulty and self-sacrifice, is so dear to Hashem. It is worth far more to Him than learning for longer hours with peace and calm."

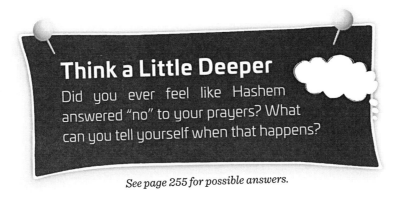

Think a Little Deeper
Did you ever feel like Hashem answered "no" to your prayers? What can you tell yourself when that happens?

See page 255 for possible answers.

POSSIBLE ANSWERS

1. The Veil

Think a Little Deeper — *Possible answers include:*

- Honeybees need nectar to produce honey. The bee has a very long, strawlike tongue that is perfect for sucking the nectar out of flowers.
- Storing the honey in wax honeycombs allows it to last throughout the cold winter.
- The honeycomb storage parts are shaped like hexagons, which is the most efficient way to maximize use of the hive's limited space.

It can only be Hashem's handiwork!

2. Cash in the Trash

Let's Talk About It — *Possible answers include:*

- Look for it, but don't be upset. Realize that it's all from Hashem.
- Pray to Hashem that you should somehow get it back.

3. Sixty-Forty

Let's Talk About It — *Possible answers include:*

- Thank You, Hashem, for giving me: (1) The Torah, (2) my family, (3) my eyes, (4) food, (5) clothing, (6) my home.
- My requests are: (1) Mashiach, (2) *refuah sheleimah* for..., (3) success in my learning, (4) help in strengthening my *emunah*.

Think a Little Deeper — *Possible answers include:*

- We become accustomed to getting good things and we expect it.
- If many people have it, it doesn't seem special to us.

4. Succah of Peace

Let's Talk About It — *Possible answers include:*

- Realize it's a test from Hashem.
- *Dan l'chaf zechus* — Judge the neighbor in a positive way.

5. Direct Line

Let's Talk About It — *Possible answers include:*

- Hashem, please help us to: (1) stay healthy, (2) have success in Torah and doing mitzvos, (3) find the right shidduch for...

6. The Tongue

Think a Little Deeper — *Possible answers include:*

- Our tongue allows us to do the mitzvah of saying good things about people and making others feel good.

7. Never Stranded

Think a Little Deeper — *Possible answers include:*

- Hashem created us with *bechirah*, free choice. He is constantly testing our *emunah*. If He always showed us how He was arranging everything, it would be so obvious that we would lose that bechirah.

8. Full circle

Let's Talk About It — *Possible answers include:*

- (1) That I am able to... (2) My family had a *simchah* this year. (3) I have great friends, neighbors, community... (4) I'm healthy!

Think a Little Deeper - Possible answers include:

- Hashem will reward us for realizing that all our blessings come from Him.
- When we thank Hashem for what He gives us, He wants to give us more.

9. Surprise!

Let's Talk About It — *Possible answers include:*

- Pray to Hashem for help.
- Leave and keep your promise. All *parnassah* comes from Hashem. You won't lose by doing the right thing.

Think a Little Deeper — *Possible answers include:*

- בְּדֶרֶךְ שֶׁאָדָם רוֹצֶה לֵילֵךְ בָּהּ מוֹלִיכִין אוֹתוֹ — If a person really wants to do good, Hashem will help. Never give up. Hashem can arrange anything!

10. Forever Indebted

Let's Talk About It — *Possible answers include:*

- We show that we realize everything we have is from Hashem, and we know that we can rely on Him for whatever we need.

11. A Closer Look

Let's Talk About It — Possible answers include:

- It's truly amazing how the eye sees something, and sends that picture to the brain where it will stay for life! It can only be Hashem!

Think a Little Deeper — Possible answers include:

- By learning about the incredible miracles of the eye, we will be grateful that we can see and be inspired to serve Hashem.

12. Bullet-Proof Tzitzis

Let's Talk About It — Possible answers include:

- Hashem wanted us to know that *tzitzis* do protect us!

Think a Little Deeper — Possible answers include:

- (1) Rico gave the Rabbi the CD's to take back to Lakewood. If not, we would never have learned this lesson. (2) The only CD that stayed intact was the one that spoke about the protection of *tzitzis*.

14. Stalled

Let's Talk About It — Possible answers include:

- (1) Don't get upset, everything is from Hashem. (2) *Gam zu letovah*; somehow it was all for the good, even if you don't understand why. (3) Be positive. *Baruch Hashem*, now the car is working and you were able to enjoy your vacation!

15. Only Hashem!

Let's Talk About It — Possible answers include:

- By constantly reviewing over and over that there is no power except for Hashem. Whether it be through stories or through our life experiences, we always have to remind ourselves: אֵין עוֹד מִלְבַדּוֹ — "There is no power other than Hashem."

16. Season of Change

Let's Talk About It — Possible answers include:

- If not for the warmer seasons, there are many different types of fruits and vegetables that wouldn't be able to grow. If not for the colder seasons we would never have snow, which is very beneficial to the ground — and a lot of fun!

Think a Little Deeper — Possible answers include:

- (1) It would be pretty boring if the weather was always the same. (2) Because of the change from season to season we appreciate the different climates.

17. Last Respects

Let's Talk About It — Possible answers include:

- (1) One mitzvah leads to another. (First he joined the *minyan* and then he had the *zechus* to do the burial.) (2) Hashem will reward us for everything we do.

18. Matzah for Eternity

Let's Talk About It — Possible answers include:

- (1) A yeshivah, since he will have the *zechus* of all the learning! (2) Since Reb Shaya didn't have children, he should give to those who are trying to have children, or to orphans. (3) Needy families, since that will bring people happiness. (4) *Hachnasas kallah*, to help a *chassan* and *kallah* get married and build a new Jewish home. (5) A shul, where so many *tefillos* will be said in his merit.

19. One Word

Let's Talk About It — Possible answers include:

- (1) It shows his love for Shabbos. (2) It shows his *yiras Shamayim*, his faith that Shabbos bears witness that Hashem created the world, so we must protect and spread observance of Shabbos. (3) It shows his love for Hashem, because he donated so much to stop people from disobeying Hashem.

  It is an act of *emunah* because only someone who truly believes in reward and punishment and knows clearly that Hashem is always watching would be able to do such a thing.

20. Just Ask

Think a Little Deeper — Possible answers include:

- If we would have only good things without praying for Hashem's blessings, we would forget that everything is a gift from Him. Hashem made the world so that we must ask Him to help us. This way we build a relationship with Him; we grow through realizing that all is from Him.

21. Beautiful Gift, Beautiful Wrapper

Let's Talk About It — Possible answers include:

- Besides that they are already prepared and pre-cut into slices, if you look you will see that each piece of orange is made up of many droplets. This gives it that extra juicy flavor! It can only be Hashem!

Think a Little Deeper — Possible answers include:

- When we study the fascinating wonders in one little piece of fruit, we will realize that it's impossible that it happened on its own. Who told the fruit to do all these things? It can only be Hashem!

22. Unlocked Opportunity

Think a Little Deeper *— Possible answers include:*

- (1) The fact that the wallet was lost made it possible for Tuvia to get a job. (2) That Tuvia was a locksmith came up in the conversation.

23. Breath of Fresh Air

Let's Talk About It *— Possible answers include:*

- When one thanks Hashem for all the blessings in his life, one is growing closer to Hashem. Constantly thanking Hashem is building our *emunah* that Hashem is the One Who gives and can give more. That growth in *emunah* turns us into better people. We are no longer the same!

Think a Little Deeper *— Possible answers include:*

- (1) Thank You, Hashem, that I can breathe normally. (2) Thank You, Hashem, that I have family. (Thank You, Hashem, that I can see... We can list a hundred things.)

24. Buried Treasure

Let's Talk About It *— Possible answers include:*

- Some people would probably get very down. They might even question Hashem and think, "After all the *tzedakah* I gave, this is what I get?" However, Hashem would want them to have *emunah* and realize that it's a test, and that sooner or later good will come out of it.

Think a Little Deeper *— Possible answers include:*

- (1) *Gam zu l'tovah!* The cow falling into the pit ended up being the biggest *berachah*. (2) Hashem rewards those who go out of their way to give *tzedakah*.

25. A Special Connection

Let's Talk About It *— Possible answers include:*

- Rabbi Lish is referring to Hashem.

Think a Little Deeper *— Possible answers include:*

- (1) *Refuah sheleimah* for... (2) Good *parnassah* for... (3) Success in learning for...

26. Beaver, Beaver, Overachiever

Let's Talk About It *— Possible answers include:*

- They thought that by bringing the beavers it would help them. They later learned that the beavers belong where Hashem put them.

Think a Little Deeper *— Possible answers include:*

- This story reminds us that Hashem arranges everything in the most perfect way — from people to the weather, planets, and even animals. Each is exactly where it should be. It can only be Hashem!

27. Stuck on the Tracks

Let's Talk About It — *Possible answers include:*

- The volunteers might think, "What a waste of time. We had to sit in all that traffic for nothing." However, with the right *emunah* in Hashem they would think, "*Gam zu l'tovah*"; or "We did the right thing; who could have known it was not serious?"; or "Hashem wanted to reward us for making a big effort to do a mitzvah."

Think a Little Deeper — *Possible answers include:*

- (1) Because they got stuck in heavy traffic on the way there, they drove by exactly when the wheelchair was stuck. If it would have been earlier or later they would not have been able to help.
- (2) The driver decided to drive by the tracks and not the other route of Ocean Avenue.

28. Congratulations!

Think a Little Deeper — *Possible answers include:*

- Thank You, Hashem, for: (1) my hands, (2) electricity, (3) my brother(s) / sister(s), (4) my taste buds.

29. Patience, My Friend

Let's Talk About It — *Possible answers include:*

- What looked to Manis as something bad or destructive ended being exactly what was needed in order to produce the delicious bread. So too, throughout our lives we must remember: Even though we don't see the good right now, in the end it will be for the best.

30. The Impossible

Let's Talk About It — *Possible answers include:*

- (1) Because they are pure and have not done any sins. (2) A child is sincere. All his feelings come from the heart.

31. Slowly but Surely

Think a Little Deeper — *Possible answers include:*

- The change from day to night and night to day. It would be very inconvenient and even dangerous if it instantly became dark at night. Also from summer to winter. It would be terrible if one day it was 90 degrees and the next day it was freezing.

32. Never Forgotten

Let's Talk About It — *Possible answers include:*

- Pray to Hashem that He should help me find the boy.

Think a Little Deeper — *Possible answers include:*

- (1) Maybe it was a test to see if the Chazon Ish would continue to try and find him. (2) Maybe the other person didn't deserve to have the money.

33. No News Is Good News

Let's Talk About It *— Possible answers include:*

- We get used to our surroundings and come to expect everything we call "normal." However, we must remember that Hashem does not owe us anything! Every moment of life is a gift from Hashem!

Think a Little Deeper *— Possible answers include:*

- (1) Thank You, Hashem, that I am able to eat. (2) Thank You, Hashem, that we have shuls. (3) Thank You, Hashem, that my heart is working!

34. Honesty Pays

Let's Talk About It *— Possible answers include:*

- To stay honest. Remember: Every penny is from Hashem! If we were supposed to have it, Hashem would give it to us.

Think a Little Deeper *— Possible answers include:*

- (1) By remaining honest I am showing that I believe that Hashem sees everything I do. (2) By remaining honest I am showing that I believe that all my money is only from Hashem and there is no reason to be dishonest. I will get exactly what was decided on Rosh Hashanah either way.

35. Bring Back Jack

Let's Talk About It *— Possible answers include:*

- By praying or doing mitzvos for his *zechus*.

36. Who Is in Charge?

Let's Talk About It *— Possible answers include:*

- (1) How amazing that every animal, bird, fish, and insect gets the food that it needs when it needs it! How is that possible?
- (2) How is it possible that the heart keeps pumping more than 100,000 times a day, even though it's not plugged into electricity?

Think a Little Deeper *— Possible answers include:*

- Hashem created the world in order to bestow goodness on us. He gives us a chance to do good things, to earn reward for the next world. He wants us to become close to Him so that we can grow and become great people.

37. Lunch Dilemma

Let's Talk About It *— Possible answers include:*

- Hashem is giving her an opportunity to speak to Him and build her *emunah* that He can help with anything, big or small.

Think a Little Deeper — Possible answers include:

- Tamar can learn that Hashem is involved in every little thing! Dina should realize that *tefillah* works! Hashem arranges everything!

38. Saved by the Queen

Let's Talk About It — Possible answers include:

- If we believe that Hashem is always here and always watching, that will give us the strength to fight the *yetzer hara*. (Think about it: If a parent or rebbi is with us, we are usually more careful with the way we act.)

Think a Little Deeper — Possible answers include:

- By keeping Shabbos we are practicing *emunah* in action! The reason why we stay away from doing any work is because Hashem rested on the seventh day. By keeping Shabbos we are proclaiming that Hashem is the Creator of the world.

39. Absolute Faith

Let's Talk About It — Possible answers include:

- He's probably thinking, *Why is my rebbi doing this?* He can strengthen his *emunah* by reminding himself that Hashem must be causing this to happen for a good reason.

40. The Small Stuff

Let's Talk About It — Possible answers include:

- (1) That my teacher give us extra recess today. (2) That my toasted bagel should come out the way I like it.

Think a Little Deeper — Possible answers include:

- (1) When we pray for "small stuff" we are showing that Hashem is in charge of even the smallest detail of our lives. (2) We are demonstrating that Hashem hears us and cares about every little need that we may have. Hashem loves us!

41. A Random Spill

Let's Talk About It — Possible answers include:

- Of course not! There is absolutely zero chance of that happening.

Think a Little Deeper — Possible answers include:

- Even something as simple as a hair shows Hashem's wondrous design.
- Each hair grows out of its own separate hair follicle.
- The hair of the eyebrows stops sweat from rolling into our eyes.
- The hairs of an eyelash protect the eye from dust and other particles in the air.
- Hair on the head grows about half an inch per month, but eyelashes and eyebrows stop growing at full length. Otherwise, we would have to get haircuts for our eyes.

42. Ready and Waiting

Let's Talk About It - Possible answers include:

- I would probably think, *why bother*. But then I might say, "What do I have to lose, I should at least try."

43. A Couple of Cups

Let's Talk About It — Possible answers include:

- When one knows that every penny he earns is directly from Hashem, he will say to himself, "Why should I lie or steal — I'm going to get the same amount either way! I will remain honest!"

Think a Little Deeper — Possible answers include:

- When we practice *emunas chachamim* we are showing that we believe that the Rabbi is a *shaliach*, agent, of Hashem. Hashem chose the *chachamim*, who are close to Him, to guide us. It's all from Hashem!

44. Do You Believe?

Let's Talk About It — Possible answers include:

- The fact that no one was willing to go shows that they didn't have 100 percent trust in him. They were sure he could cross safely, but not so sure that they would risk their lives.

Think a Little Deeper — Possible answers include:

- If we believe that Hashem can do anything, that Hashem loves us and wants the best for us, we will be calm and relaxed.

45. Last Minute

Let's Talk About It — Possible answers include:

- At first I might get nervous. However, I would try to remind myself that Hashem would want me to trust in Him, to rely on Him, and ask Him for help. Never give up! Hashem can do anything!

46. Chew Over It

Let's Talk About It — Possible answers include:

- If the molars were in front it would be very hard to bite into food. Hashem positioned each tooth in the perfect spot.

Think a Little Deeper — Possible answers include:

- When we talk about the wonders of Hashem, like the teeth, we realize His greatness. We strengthen our *emunah* — it can only be Hashem!

47. Two Lucky Winners

Let's Talk About It — Possible answers include:

- Hashem cares for the feelings of even a small child. He arranged for Malka to also be a winner in the raffle so she should not be disappointed.

48. Big Deal

Let's Talk About It — Possible answers include:

- Anytime we receive anything from anyone we have to be thankful and show appreciation.

49. Today Is the Day

Let's Talk About It — Possible answers include:

- (1) I can see! (2) I have friends! (3) I have Torah!

50. Whatever the Weather

Let's Talk About It — Possible answers include:

- (1) Pray to Hashem for help. (2) Don't be down. Hashem only wants us to do our best. He rewards us for effort.

51. Take a Deep Breath

Let's Talk About It — Possible answers include:

- We need: (1) the sun, (2) water, (3) food.

52. Hot Water

Let's Talk About It — Possible answers include:

- (1) Pray to Hashem for help. (2) Don't get nervous; rely on Hashem. (3) Say *Gam zu l'tovah.*

Think a Little Deeper — Possible answers include:

- Every time we hear a story of *hashgachah,* we are reminded that Hashem is always in total control and can do anything at any time for anyone! These reminders will help us be prepared next time we are faced with a challenge.

53. Chasing the Moon

Let's Talk About It — Possible answers include:

- When people go out of their way for someone or something, that shows their love. By running after a mitzvah from which one is exempt, one is building his connection with Hashem.

Think a Little Deeper — Possible answers include:

- (Example) One time it was late at night when I realized that I didn't daven Maariv yet. I got up and went to look for a *minyan.* It was not easy, but once I did it, I felt a stronger connection with Hashem.

54. Six Precious Months

Let's Talk About It — Possible answers include:

- We cannot understand the ways of Hashem. Hashem has his reasons for why that tragedy had to happen. Rabbi Balk needs to believe that it would have happened either way.

55. Garden of Miracles

Let's Talk About It — *Possible answers include:*

- The garden might have grown without the children praying. However, with every prayer to Hashem they were building their *emunah* that the garden can grow only if Hashem says it should. The garden was there to give them a chance to pray.

Think a Little Deeper — *Possible answers include:*

- They learn that Hashem is not involved only in the "big things" or with "big people," but even in the little things as well. Hashem is directly involved in every aspect of our lives, big or small.

56. The Nose Knows

Let's Talk About It — *Possible answers include:*

- Hashem wants us to be happy and enjoy His beautiful world.

Think a Little Deeper — *Possible answers include:*

- By studying the wonders of the nose we will realize how amazing and helpful is our sense of smell. We have the opportunity to grow closer to Hashem every time we smell! It can only be Hashem!

57. Circle of Kindness

Let's Talk About It — *Possible answers include:*

- If someone did an act of *chesed* for us, we need to realize that Hashem sent him as His *shaliach* (messenger). I must be very grateful to the person who Hashem sent to help me. I must also realize that Hashem was the One Who directed it all.

58. The Gift of *Teshuvah*

Let's Talk About It — *Possible answers include:*

- *Teshuvah* is possible only if I believe in Hashem. My belief that Hashem is here and that Hashem loves me will give me the strength to ask for forgivness.
- There is another aspect of *emunah* with regard to *teshuvah*: I have to have the *emunah* that Hashem can absolutely erase whatever wrong I might have done, so that I will be able to serve Him with a clean slate. Thank you Hashem!

59. A Warm Gesture

Let's Talk About It — *Possible answers include:*

- It might not be easy, but Klal Yisrael is always looking to do *chesed*. Therefore, it would be the right thing to help, even the competition.

Think a Little Deeper — *Possible answers include:*

- Absolutely not! We have to constantly remind ourselves that every penny we earn is from Hashem. In the end we will make exactly the amount that Hashem decides, no matter what!

60. The Secret Mitzvah Chain

Let's Talk About It — *Possible answers include:*

- When we do a mitzvah that no one knows about it shows that we are doing it only for Hashem.

Think a Little Deeper — *Possible answers include:*

- (Pause for a while.) Okay, let's keep it between you and Hashem! (Maybe taking out the heavy garbage cans for your elderly neighbor when nobody is around to see you?)

61. Crystal Clear

Let's Talk About It — *Possible answers include:*

- By having more *kavanah* (thought) next time we make a *berachah* on a glass of water.

Think a Little Deeper — *Possible answers include:*

- (1) When we drink water it doesn't leave any aftertaste. (2) Because it's tasteless it doesn't cancel out the taste of the delicious food you just ate.

62. Fully Stocked

Let's Talk About It — *Possible answers include:*

- (1) Sponsor a *kiddush* when you get back home. (2) When eating that food say the *berachos* clearly and with concentration.

Think a Little Deeper — *Possible answers include:*

- (1) The hotel gave him that room. (2) The food was kosher. (3) The food was fresh. (4) He chose that hotel. (5) The other person ran out without taking his food.

63. Offer of a Lifetime

Let's Talk About It — *Possible answers include:*

- The king is Hashem. The peasant is Bnei Yisrael, that means us. The jobs are the mitzvos and the reward is to be close to Hashem in *Olam Haba*, the Next World. The week of paid vacation is Shabbos.

Think a Little Deeper — *Possible answers include:*

- Every time we do a mitzvah we are showing *emunah* in action! Think about it. The only reason why he's putting on his *tzitzis* or shaking his *lulav* or doing any mitzvah is because Hashem commanded us. When I do a mitzvah I am saying, "I believe in You, Hashem, and that's why I'm doing this."

64. Detour by Design

Think a Little Deeper — *Possible answers include:*

- There can be many reasons. (1) To avoid an accident. (2) The inconvenience will be a *kapparah* for something we did wrong. (3) Hashem wants you to meet someone who won't be there until a little later. (4) It's an opportunity to grow in *emunah* and trust in Hashem.

65. A Protective Shield

Let's Talk About It — Possible answers include:

- (1) He should be the one to pray for the family. (2) Do *teshuvah*. (3) Give *tzedakah*.

66. First Line of Defense

Let's Talk About It — Possible answers include:

- Without the sense of touch I might not know if something was hot or cold.

Think a Little Deeper — Possible answers include:

- By learning about our wondrous skin, we are learning about Hashem! Hashem's wisdom is in every creation. As we learn, we gain more knowledge and become more aware of Hashem's greatness.

67. Stuck in a Truck

Let's Talk About It — Possible answers include:

- As long as it's safe, Hashem would want me to try and help. Hashem let me see that for a reason. *There is no such thing as coincidence!*

68. At Your Fingertips

Let's Talk About It — Possible answers include:

- Without your fingers, it would be impossible to: (1) write, (2) hold a glass, (3) turn pages in a book, (4) hold cutlery when you eat, (5) dial a phone number.

Think a Little Deeper — Possible answers include:

- By keeping my finger on the place when my rebbi/morah is teaching me Torah.

69. Long-Term Benefit

Let's Talk About It — Possible answers include:

- That everything Hashem does to us is ultimately for our good, even if right now it seems bad.

70. Investment to Bank on

Let's Talk About It — Possible answers include:

- (1) Pray to Hashem that it should somehow work out. (2) Stay and rely on Hashem. (3) Say and think *Ein od milvado!*

Think a Little Deeper — Possible answers include:

- In order to let us earn His reward. Hashem set up the world so that we would have *bechirah*, free choice to decide if we want to do good or bad. With the ability to choose on our own, we can earn the greatest reward if we choose to do the right thing.

71. The Incredible Fork

Let's Talk About It — *Possible answers include:*

- No way! The chances of that happening are one in many billions — it's impossible!

Think a Little Deeper — *Possible answers include:*

- He was teaching them that obviously there is a Creator. Believe it or not, there are those in the world who would like to believe that everything in the universe just happened by accident. We all agree that a simple plastic fork could not have been formed from that explosion. How much more so an eye, a heart, the sun, trees, or anything else in our beautiful world. It can only be Hashem!

72. It Could Have Been Me

Let's Talk About It — *Possible answers include:*

- We are reminded that there is no such thing as coincidence! Hashem runs the world.

Think a Little Deeper — *Possible answers include:*

- He must be so grateful to Hashem for saving him! He should strengthen his *emunah* in Hashem. He should realize how much Hashem loves him.

73. How Can I Ever Repay You?

Let's Talk About It — *Possible answers include:*

- By using our eyes the way Hashem wants us to.

Think a Little Deeper — *Possible answers include:*

- (1) Learn Hashem's Torah. (2) Say the *berachah* of פּוֹקֵחַ עִוְרִים, *Gives sight to the blind,* with *kavanah.* (3) By not looking at anything Hashem doesn't approve of.

74. A New Lease on Life

Let's Talk About It — *Possible answers include:*

- The only way he was able to keep going was by understanding that Hashem is with him. He believed that Hashem was testing him. Hashem wants us to rely on Him!

Think a Little Deeper — *Possible answers include:*

- If not for his *emunah* that Hashem would help him, he would have gone back home to Lithuania. Who knows what would have happened to Rav Eliyahu once the Nazis *y"sh* came in? But now that he went to England, he was safe and was able to teach Torah to thousands of people.

75. I Just Want to Hear Your Voice

Think a Little Deeper — *Possible answers include:*

- If we truly believe that Hashem loves us, hears us, and can do anything, that will inspire us to do *teshuvah.*

76. The Real Deal

Let's Talk About It — Possible answers include:

- Aaron is forgetting that every single penny that a person earns is directly from Hashem. True, we have to do our part (*hishtadlus*); however, in the end it is all from Hashem. This is one of the things that we must always remember: "Hashem is the One Who gives us the ability to do our business." We have to know that even the decision to buy or sell… when and what etc., is all from Hashem!

77. Mini-Miracle

Let's Talk About It — Possible answers include:

- Hashem could have dealt with us on a very general, far-removed level. However, Hashem chose to be directly involved in every aspect of our lives. That shows His care and love for each of us.

78. Great Idea!

Let's Talk About It — Possible answers include:

- (1) I can think of how to answer this question. (2) I can learn Hashem's Torah. (3) I can walk and talk.

Think a Little Deeper — Possible answers include:

- By using our minds to serve Hashem: (1) learning His Torah, (2) judging people favorably, (3) thinking about the greatness of Hashem, (4) training our minds to rely on and trust in Hashem.

79. Irreplaceable Loyalty

Let's Talk About It — Possible answers include:

- She might be thinking, "Maybe I need the merit of doing this *chesed* of babysitting and I should miss the appointment. On the other hand, maybe Hashem wants me to do my part. Hashem gave me this appointment, so maybe I shouldn't miss it." Not an easy decision!

80. Car Colors

Let's Talk About It — Possible answers include:

- Hashem wants us to daven to Him for every little thing! When we daven for the "small" things, that shows that we believe that Hashem is involved in every aspect of our lives.

Think a Little Deeper — Possible answers include:

- (1) That my lunch should come out the way I like it. (2) That I should win the game. (3) That I should get a good mark on the test. (4) That my parents should enjoy their vacation.

81. Pumped!

Let's Talk About It — *Possible answers include:*

- It is amazing how the heart can keep on pumping for so many years, without needing any maintenance. It can only be Hashem!

Think a Little Deeper — *Possible answers include:*

- We need to realize that our life, our body with all its organs, are gifts from Hashem. By taking care of our health, we are saying, "Hashem, I know this body is a gift from You." That will strengthen our *emunah*.

82. Captured by a Picture

Let's Talk About It — *Possible answers include:*

- (1) The photographer chose that boy to take a picture of. (2) The photographer was there at the same time as the boy while he was davening.

83. Thank You, Hashem, Again and Again

Let's Talk About It — *Possible answers include:*

- (1) *Gam zu l'tovah*. (2) Stay calm — realize it's a test from Hashem. (3) Pray to Hashem for help.

Think a Little Deeper — *Possible answers include:*

- There is no such thing as coincidence! Hashem was showing Mr. Harary that He was with him! That he reacted the right way. He passed the test! It was like a big hug from Hashem.

84. The Winning Ticket

Let's Talk About It — *Possible answers include:*

- We have to believe that Hashem decides how much money a person will receive. Meir was supposed to win the raffle, so he got the winning ticket, and Hashem let Yisrael be the one to give him the ticket.

85. In the Blink of an Eye

Let's Talk About It — *Possible answers include:*

- The normal reaction would be disappointment. One might even become depressed and give up all hope. However, the way Hashem would want one to react is with *emunah*. To continue to call out to Hashem, strengthening one's *emunah* that Hashem can do anything. That's what Rabbi Rubashkin did and Hashem rewarded him for it.

Think a Little Deeper — *Possible answers include:*

- The only way one can be prepared for such a test is by constantly learning about *emunah*. By talking and reading about *emunah* and *bitachon* we become more ready to deal with challenges.

86. Win-Win

Let's Talk About It *— Possible answers include:*

- By discussing wonders in the animal world we come to realize more and more of Hashem's greatness.

Think a Little Deeper *— Possible answers include:*

- It is truly amazing how each animal is in the perfect setting and climate.

87. Odd Number, Breaking Even

Let's Talk About It *— Possible answers include:*

- With *emunah* you know that you will not lose out. Hashem has no limits; He can pay us back in the most marvelous ways.

88. A Cool Invention

Let's Talk About It *— Possible answers include:*

- Hashem loves us and wants us to enjoy His world.

Think a Little Deeper *— Possible answers include:*

- Candy. Watermelon. All the different flavored snacks. Tasty, healthy food.

89. Precious Lashes

Let's Talk About It *— Possible answers include:*

- What he thought was bad ended up being good. *Gam zu l'tovah.*

Think a Little Deeper *— Possible answers include:*

- Somehow this is for my best. I trust Hashem and I know that He loves me very much.

90. A Plea From the Heart

Let's Talk About It *— Possible answers include:*

- The fact that he's asking shows that he believes Hashem can help. You ask only if you believe that someone is listening and capable.

Think a Little Deeper *— Possible answers include:*

- Through prayer we become more aware of Hashem. It builds our relationship with Him. In that merit He can change any decree.

91. Symptoms of Love

Think a Little Deeper *— Possible answers include:*

- When one feels pain as a warning sign, that reminds one that everything is set up with a plan and purpose. Hashem runs the most perfect system!

92. Just in Time

Let's Talk About It *— Possible answers include:*

- The chances of that specific CD with the honking sound playing at exactly at the perfect moment are one in a million. It can only be Hashem!

93. Smoothing Over the Cracks

Let's Talk About It — *Possible answers include:*

- (1) *Gam zu l'tovah.* (2) Pray to Hashem for help.

Think a Little Deeper — *Possible answers include:*

- We can't know if they would have repaved or not. However, if Yehoshua had continued to complain, we do know that he would have missed out on amazing growth. The connection that comes through calling out to Hashem, and then being answered, is priceless!

94. The Judge Is...

Let's Talk About It — *Possible answers include:*

- (1) He will pray even harder now. (2) Maybe this young replacement lawyer will do better than his original lawyer.

Think a Little Deeper — *Possible answers include:*

- The fact that his original lawyer got delayed ended up being the best thing for him.

95. From the Heart

Let's Talk About It — *Possible answers include:*

- We are here in this world in order to become aware of Hashem. Sometimes He might hold things back from us in order that we should pray and rely on Him. Through asking, we build our *emunah* that everything is in His hands.

Think a Little Deeper — *Possible answers include:*

- Not necessarily. They could have taken the food with them, or they could have given it to a different neighbor.

96. Tap, Tap, Tap

Let's Talk About It — *Possible answers include:*

- The woodpecker, like all birds and animals, gives us the opportunity to see the greatness of Hashem in the world. Every time we see the amazing wonders of Hashem we come to realize His endless wisdom and come to love Him more and more.

Think a Little Deeper — *Possible answers include:*

- Hashem created the woodpecker with exactly every detail that it needs. The same is true of every creation in the world. We can take that lesson into our lives as well. We each have exactly what is best for us.

97. Perfect Payback

Let's Talk About It — *Possible answers include:*

- (1) He saw the sign. (2) The topic was *kiddush Hashem*. (3) The Rabbi was the driver.

Think a Little Deeper — *Possible answers include:*

- We must remember that Hashem has every detail recorded. Everything will be repaid at some time. Never lose the *emunah* that Hashem will reward us for every mitzvah.

98. For Problems Too

Let's Talk About It — *Possible answers include:*

- Maybe Hashem is testing my *emunas chachamim*; will I question the *gadol* or will I trust that he is a messenger of Hashem?

99. A Golden Opportunity

Let's Talk About It — *Possible answers include:*

- (1) Say and think *Gam zu l'tovah*. (2) Realize it's a test from Hashem. (3) Strengthen my belief that it wasn't meant for me; every penny is from Hashem.

100. Hashem said, "No."

Let's Talk About It — *Possible answers include:*

- His *emunah* is being tested. We have to trust that Hashem knows what we need to fulfill our mission in this world.

Think a Little Deeper — *Possible answers include:*

- Hashem can do anything. Hashem loves me very, very much. If Hashem said, "No," I have to accept that this is the best answer for me.

This volume is part of
THE ARTSCROLL® SERIES
an ongoing project of
translations, commentaries and expositions on
Scripture, Mishnah, Talmud, Midrash, Halachah,
liturgy, history, the classic Rabbinic writings,
biographies and thought.

For a brochure of current publications
visit your local Hebrew bookseller
or contact the publisher:

Mesorah Publications, ltd

313 Regina Avenue
Rahway, New Jersey 07065
(718) 921-9000
www.artscroll.com